WITHDRAWN

DATE DUE

CUTTING THE ROSE

FEMALE GENITAL MUTILATION:

THE PRACTICE AND

ITS PREVENTION

Minority Rights Group is an international, non-governmental organization whose aims are to ensure justice for minority (and non-dominant majority) groups suffering discrimination by:

1. Researching and publishing the facts as widely as possible to raise public knowledge and awareness of minority issues worldwide.

2. Advocating on all aspects of human rights of minorities to aid the prevention of dangerous and destructive conflicts.

3. Educating through its schools programme on issues relating to prejudice, discrimination and group conflicts.

If you would like to know more about the work of Minority Rights Group, please contact Alan Phillips (Director), MRG, 379 Brixton Road, London SW9 7DE, United Kingdom.

m

Minority Rights Publications is a series of books from Minority Rights Group. Through the series, we aim to make available to a wide audience reliable data on, and objective analyses of, specific minority issues. The series draws on the expertise and authority built up by Minority Rights Group over two decades of publishing.

Other titles in the book series are:

Armenia and Karabagh: The Struggle for Unity
Edited by Christopher J. Walker (1991)

The Kurds: A Nation Denied
by David McDowall (1992)

Refugees: Asylum in Europe?
by Danièle Joly *et al* (1992)

The Balkans: Minorities and States in Conflict, 2nd Edition
by Hugh Poulton (1993)

Polar Peoples – Self-Determination and Development
by Beach, Creery, Korsmo, Nuttall, Vakhtin (1994)

The Palestinians – The Road to Nationhood
by David McDowall (1994)

CUTTING THE ROSE

FEMALE GENITAL MUTILATION:

THE PRACTICE AND

ITS PREVENTION

by
Efua Dorkenoo

Minority Rights Publications

© Minority Rights Group 1994

First published in the United Kingdom
in 1994 by
Minority Rights Publications
379 Brixton Road
London SW9 7DE

British Library Cataloguing in Publication Data
A CIP catalogue record of this book is available from the British Library.

ISBN 1 873194 60 9 hardback

Library of Congress Cataloguing in Publication Data
CIP Data available from the Library of Congress

Cover design by Wave Design
Typeset by Brixton Graphics in Stone Serif 9¼ pt
Printed on chlorine-free paper in the UK by Redwood Books

Cover photo of girls in Mali
© Marc Schlossman

CONTENTS

LIST OF MAPS & ILLUSTRATIONS   vi
ACKNOWLEDGEMENTS   vii

1   Introduction   1

2   The practice   29

3   What are the issues?   43

4   International initiatives and action   59

5   Africa – case studies   83

6   Western countries and prevention   123

7   Conclusions and directions for the future   161

APPENDIX   177
NOTES AND REFERENCES   180
SELECT BIBLIOGRAPHY   189
INDEX   191

Maps & Illustrations

Maps

1   Female genital mutilation in Africa and
the Middle East   ·   viii

2   Female genital mutilation in Latin America   ix

3   Female genital mutilation in India, Pakistan,
Malaysia and Indonesia   x

4   Female genital mutilation in North America,
Australia and Western Europe   xi

Illustrations

1   Normal adolescent vulva   6

2   Infibulated vulva   7

3   Extended infibulated vulva   11

4   Parting of the lips of the vulva   18

5   Clitoral 'legs'   19

Tables

1   Estimated prevalence of female genital
mutilation in Africa   91

2   How female genital mutilation is sustained
at grass roots level   88-89

3   How a child protection system for female
genital mutilation should work   142

ACKNOWLEDGEMENTS

I would like to thank Dr Scilla Elworthy for the original report, *Female Genital Mutilation*, which gave me a foundation to build on and also for being my mentor. The director, Alan Phillips, and staff at MRG for being supportive of my work over the past 14 years and, in particular, Judith Kendra, the editor, for her patience in preparing this book.

I would also like to thank Adwoa Kluvitse, Lambeth Council, London; Amna A.R. Hassan, Sudan National Committee on Traditional Practices, Khartoum; Berhane Ras-Work, President of the Inter-African Committee; the London Black Women's Health Action Project, and Jessica Neuwirth of Equality Now, New York, for their extremely useful comments on the draft of this book.

I would like to thank the Department of Health and the City Parochial Foundation, UK and the following: Lord Kennet, British House of Lords; Ben Whitaker, Director of Gulbenkian Foundation; Safiatu Singheteh, executive member of the Inter-Africa Committee, the Gambia; Osman Seguleh, community leader, Somali Community Central London; Anna-Lena Bergman, Associate Professional Officer, Division of Family Health, the World Health Organization (WHO), Geneva; Awa Thiam, president of CAMS-International, Senegal; Dr Asma El Dareer, medical doctor and writer, Sudan; Gloria Steinem and Alice Walker for their unwavering support for the anti-FGM campaign.

Also my colleague, Enyo Afele, for putting up with me as did all members of FORWARD International, especially the young women whom I have counselled.

Finally, I must thank my family, particularly my two sons, Kobina and Ebow, for tolerating my absences whilst working on this book.

Minority Rights Group would like to thank all supporters of its work, in particular Community Aid Abroad, Save The Children Fund and Christian Aid, who contributed to the production of this book.

Female Genital Mutilation
in Africa & The Middle East

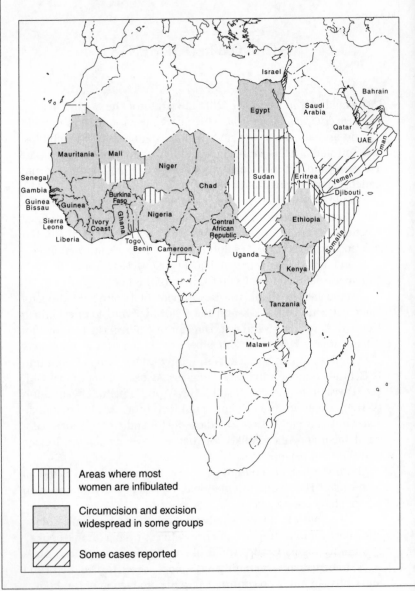

Areas where most
women are infibulated

Circumcision and excision
widespread in some groups

Some cases reported

Source: The Author / Fran Hosken

Female Genital Mutilation
in Latin America

Clitoridectomy reported to be practised by some indigenous groups.
Shaded dots represent countries involved, not exact location.

Source: The Author

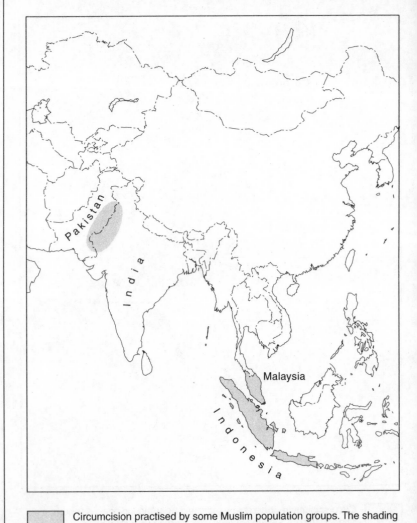

Female Genital Mutilation in India, Pakistan, Malaysia & Indonesia

Circumcision practised by some Muslim population groups. The shading in Pakistan and India represents Bohra Muslims, not exact location.

Source: The Author

*Female Genital Mutilation
in North America, Australia and Western Europe*

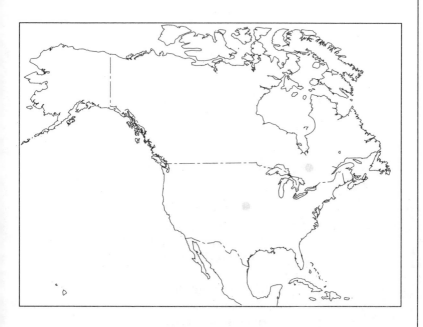

Circumcision, excision and infibulation reported
to be practised by some African immigrant population groups.
Shaded dots represent countries involved, not exact location.

Source: The Author

The sick rose

O Rose thou art sick!
The invisible worm
That flies in the night
In the howling storm

Has found out thy bed
Of crimson joy:
And his dark secret love
Does thy life destroy.

William Blake

1

INTRODUCTION

'The little girl, entirely nude, is immobilized in the sitting position on a low stool by at least three women. One of them with her arms tightly around the little girl's chest; two others hold the child's thighs apart by force, in order to open wide the vulva. The child's arms are tied behind her back, or immobilized by two other women guests.

The traditional operator says a short prayer: "Allah is great and Mahomet is his prophet. May Allah keep away all evils." Then she spreads on the floor some offerings to Allah: split maize or, in urban areas, eggs. Then the old woman takes her razor and excises the clitoris. The infibulation follows: the operator cuts with her razor from top to bottom of the small lip and then scrapes the flesh from the inside of the large lip. This nymphectomy and scraping are repeated on the other side of the vulva.

The little girl howls and writhes in pain, although strongly held down. The operator wipes the blood from the wound and the mother, as well as the guests,"verify" her work, sometimes putting their fingers in. The amount of scraping of the large lips depends upon the "technical" ability of the operator. The opening left for urine and menstrual blood is minuscule.

Then the operator applies a paste and ensures the adhesion of the large lips by means of an acacia thorn, which pierces one lip and passes through into the other. She sticks in three or four in this *manner down the vulva. These thorns are then held in place either by means of sewing thread, or with horse-hair. Paste is again put on the wound.*

But all this is not sufficient to ensure the coalescence of the large lips; so the little girl is then tied up from her pelvis to her feet: strips of material rolled up into a rope immobilize her legs entirely. Exhausted, the little girl is then dressed and put on a bed. The operation lasts from 15 to 20 minutes according to the ability of the old woman and the resistance put up by the child.'

This description, by M.A.S. Mustafa, is recounted in the thesis of Dr Alan David, working in his home territory of Djibouti,[1] and is similar to the descriptions by anthropologist Annie de Villeneuve,[2] and by Jacques Lantier in *La Cité Magique*.[3]

Sexuality remains for many an obscure area, mined with cultural taboos, loaded with anxiety and fear. This is one of the reasons why the subject of genital mutilations provokes violent emotive reactions, both from those in the West who are shocked and indignant, and from those in Africa and the Middle East who are shocked and hurt when these facts are mentioned, and prefer to minimize the quantitative importance of the practice. Medically unnecessary, painful and extremely dangerous, these operations continue today and have affected millions of women.

Twenty-two years ago, while studying obstetrics in the UK as part of my training to become a nurse, I was suddenly thrown into a situation for which I was not prepared. An African woman had been admitted to the labour ward: she was about to deliver and had undergone the radical form of female genital mutilation as described above. She came from a community where it was an accepted norm to infibulate all girls. What was left of her natural external genitals was a mass of scar tissue with only a small opening, hardly enough to admit the little finger. Without splitting the vulval scars, there was no space for the baby to be delivered. This threw the midwives and obstetricians into panic as they were not familiar with this practice and none of them knew how to deliver her so the baby was born by Caesarean section.

She had a little girl. There were no midwifery/obstetric policies or protocols on the specialized care of infibulated women in childbirth nor on prevention. Everything was 'hush hush': 'It is a sensitive issue, we must not interfere', 'It is their culture'. Things have not changed very much today. I have often wondered what happened to the little girl. Did she too undergo infibulation?

This woman's suffering, giving birth and yet having her life-giving canal sealed by this brutal practice, haunted me and this started my quest to find out more about female genital mutilation (FGM). I went to my own roots in Ghana to discover that up to 30 per cent of Ghanaian girls and women undergo clitoridectomy. This subject came up again while I was studying at the School of Hygiene and Tropical Medicine, London. A colleague mentioned that he was contemplating sending his six year old daughter back home to Sierra Leone to undergo clitoridectomy. This stimulated much debate in my group and as most of us were health professionals, we were able to dissuade him from his plan and at least the little girl was saved for the time being. We were anxious to know more and prevailed upon a colleague from Tanzania, a public health doctor who is familiar with this topic, to give us an informal lecture on FGM. That was when I realized the scale of the problem and how deep-rooted the practice was.

I have spent the last fourteen years working on women's health issues. This has taken me on a journey into women's history and lives, working with women across cultures, particularly with those who have undergone female genital mutilation. There are many casualties whose suffering is often forgotten when this issue comes up for discussion. I have been a surrogate mother and a counsellor to many young women whose personal relationships have been blighted by this practice. The urgency for concerted effort for the eradication of FGM cannot be over-stressed if we are to save millions of little girls from undergoing it.

FGM is not a disease *per se* but a complex social practice. To attack it at its roots we need to understand why people practise it despite its numerous health consequences, and we need also to develop skills to prevent it. Over the last ten years a considerable amount of ground has been covered, particularly by African women's organizations and by non-governmental and international agencies. There are many lessons to be learnt from their experience but they are fragmented. I intend to bring all these experiences together, identify the gaps and make some suggestions to build on existing strategies for prevention which, if implemented at community, national and international level, will end the genital mutilation of girls.

WHAT IS FEMALE GENITAL MUTILATION?

It has taken people many years to start using the terminology 'female genital mutilation' (FGM) as opposed to the euphemistic term 'female circumcision'. There has been much misinformation perpetuated through the use of different terms but what is absolutely clear is that in medical terms what we are talking about is a mutilation rather than the softer concept of 'circumcision'. I support Zwang's definition that:

> *'Any definitive and irremediable removal of a healthy organ is a mutilation. The female external genital organ normally is constituted by the vulva, which comprises the labia majora, the labia minora or nymphae, and the clitoris covered by its prepuce, in front of the vestibule to the urinary meatus and the vaginal orifice. Their constitution in female humans is genetically programmed and is identically reproduced in all the embryos and in all races. The vulva is an integral part of the natural inheritance of humanity. When normal, there is absolutely no reason, medical, moral, or aesthetic, to suppress all or any part of these exterior genital organs.'*

FGM is performed to suppress and to control the sexual behaviour of girls and women. Another statement underlining the view that FGM is an abusive practice on girls came from the First Study Conference on Genital Mutilation of Girls in Europe organized by the Foundation For Women's Health Research and Development (FORWARD) in July 1992. The 'London Declaration' which emanated from the conference defines genital mutilation as the 'removal of, or injury to, any part of the female genital organ which the conference defines as a violation of the basic human rights of the girl child, which should be abolished'.[5]

Types of mutilations

There is growing evidence that wide variations of mutilation are performed on the normal female vulva in different countries but that they have been classified in different ways over the years. There is a need for standardization in this area but in its absence the following categories are presented:

1 **Circumcision**, or the removal of the prepuce or hood of the clitoris. Circumcision is the mildest type of mutilation and affects only a small proportion of the millions of women concerned. It is the type of mutilation which can correctly be called circumcision and could be described as equivalent to male circumcision, but there has been a tendency to group all kinds of mutilations under the misleading term 'female circumcision'. Biologically, the male equivalent of mutilation beyond circumcision as described would be various degrees of penisectomy – removal of the male sexual organ.

2 **Excision**, meaning partial or total cutting of the clitoris and all or part of the labia minora. In some cases the labia majora are removed but with no stitching.[6] Excision is the most widespread type of mutilation. Approximately 80 per cent of those affected undergo excision.

3 **Infibulation**, the cutting of the clitoris, labia minora and at least the anterior two-thirds and often the whole of the medial part of the labia majora. The two sides of the vulva are then pinned together by silk or catgut sutures, or thorns, thus obliterating the vaginal introitus except for a small opening, preserved by the insertion of a tiny piece of wood or reed for the passage of urine or menstrual blood. The girl's legs are then bound together from hip to ankle and she is kept immobile for up to forty days to permit the formation of scar tissue. In some communities there is no stitching but, to facilitate healing, the raw edges of the wound are brought together by adhesive substances such as eggs, sugar or acacia tar and the girl is kept immobile. In rare cases animal excreta is placed on the wound as has been observed among some people in Western Sudan.[7]

4 **Intermediate infibulation** entails different forms of mutila-

FIGURE 1
Normal adolescent vulva (in extension)
Illustrations by Fiona MacVicar / The InkShed

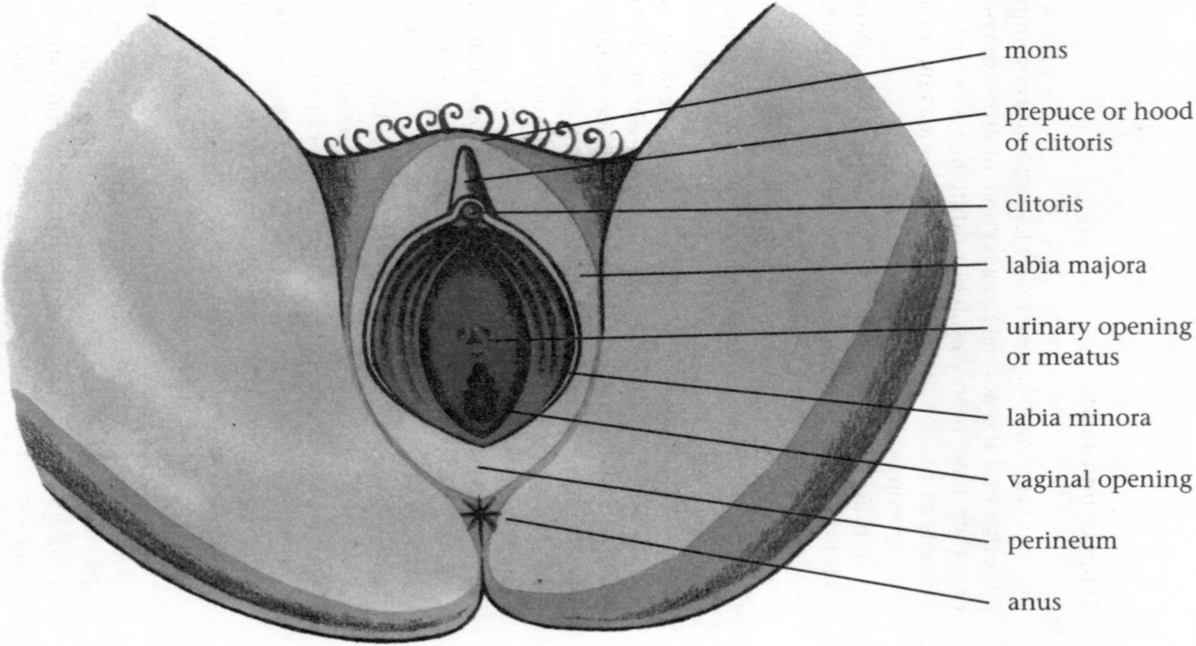

mons

prepuce or hood
of clitoris

clitoris

labia majora

urinary opening
or meatus

labia minora

vaginal opening

perineum

anus

FIGURE 2
Infibulated vulva

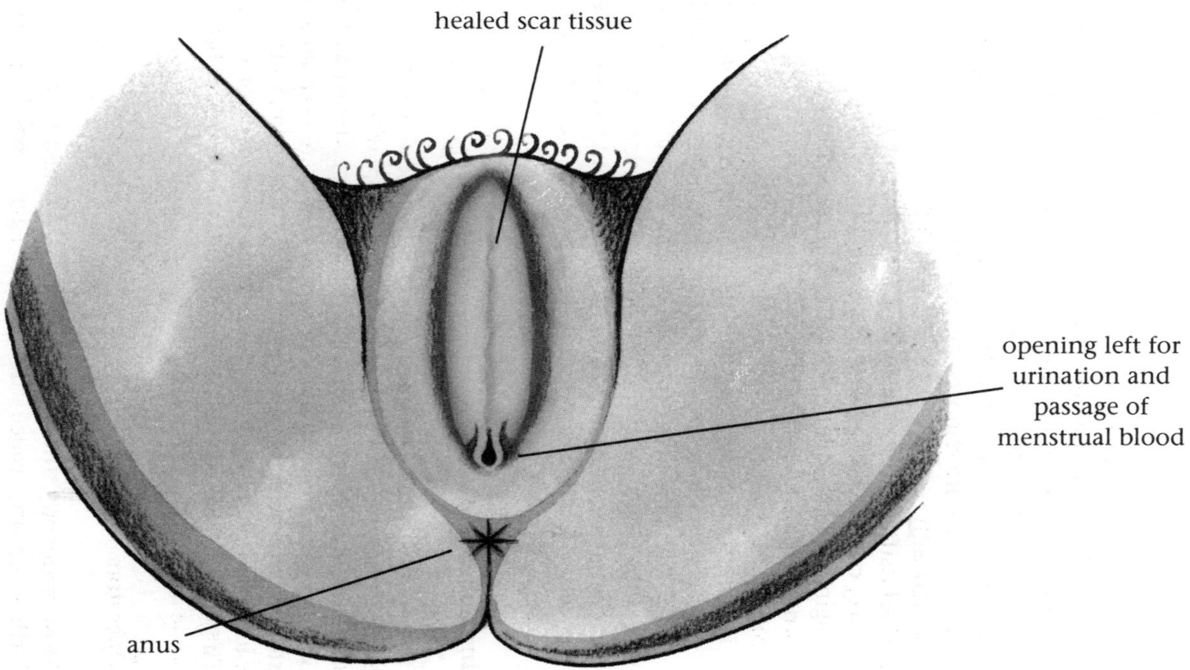

opening left for
urination and
passage of
menstrual blood

healed scar tissue

anus

tion followed by variable degrees of stitching. In one type the clitoris is removed and the surface of the labia minora roughened to allow stitching.[8] In other types, the clitoris is left intact but the labia minora are removed. The insides of the labia majora are removed and stitched with the clitoris buried underneath.

5 **Unclassified**. These include scarification of the clitoral prepuce, cuts into the clitoris and labia minora as well as into the vagina, for example, *gishiri* cuts (as practised in parts of northern Nigeria) and hymenectomy.

Sunna

Female circumcision, partial clitoridectomy, total clitoridectomy and cuts into the clitoris and even intermediate infibulation are sometimes referred to as '*sunna*' (tradition) by Muslims. Because of the variation in the types of FGM under the term '*sunna* circumcision', it is important to check precisely what people are referring to when they use the term to describe female genital mutilation.

Instruments used

These mutilations are performed with special knives (among some tribes in Mali, a saw-toothed knife),[9] with razor blades (among some tribes in Sudan, a special razor known as *Moos el Shurfa*), with pieces of glass or scissors. On rare occasions sharp stones have been reported to be used (in Eastern Sudan)[10] and cauterization (burning) is practised in some parts of Ethiopia.[11] Fingernails have been used to pluck out the clitoris of babies (in some areas in the Gambia).[12]

Operators

Most frequently, the operations are performed by a traditional birth attendant, called the *Daya* in Egypt and the Sudan. In Somalia excisors are from the *midgan* clan. In northern Nigeria, Egypt and Nigeria, male barbers also carry out the task, but usually it is done by a woman; rarely by the mother. In Mali, Senegal and the Gambia it is traditionally carried out by a woman of the blacksmith's caste gifted with knowledge of the occult. In the Gambia, they are called the *ngansingbas*.

In urban areas, female genital mutilations are being performed in hospitals or in private with anaesthetics by Western-trained doctors, nurses and midwives. Aside from the economic aspects, the justification given for medicalization of female genital mutilation is that it is better to perform the mutilation in a hygienic environment to avoid infections, to control pain and to encourage the less drastic forms of mutilation as a first step towards its eradication.

Regulation versus abolition debate

There is currently no evidence to show that a policy of promoting the less drastic forms of female genital mutilation in hygienic surroundings has led to its eradication. For example, Sudan has had a policy permitting clitoridectomy but not infibulation for nearly five decades, but there continues to be a high prevalence of female genital mutilation (89 per cent), predominantly infibulation. In Djibouti, where a clinic is run by Union Nationale des Femmes de Djibouti, a 'mild' form of female genital mutilation is performed under local anaesthetic by a traditional excisor. The women's organization believes that it can encourage the less radical forms through control in the clinic. However, it is reported that after the girls are taken home the grandmothers complain that the mutilation was not complete enough, since no infibulation was performed and the girls are re-mutilated.[13] In Kenya in 1956, Meru and Embu Council passed a law forbidding FGM but, finding that people were still performing FGM, resolved instead to educate excisors on how to perform less severe forms of FGM.[14] This was their finding:

> *'By and by it was noted that the circumcisers who had been given permits by medical officers did not carry out their duties in accordance with the instructions given them and the medical department decided not to give further courses of instructions. For that reason the council unanimously agreed that female circumcision in Embu District should be abolished.'*[15]

Due to the above experiences many experts have pressed for total abolition. They believe that if room is left for any form of mutilation, it will be difficult to monitor and therefore control its severity.[16] The public may also view medicalization of female genital mutilation as giving a green light for its continuation.As outlined earlier, genital mutilation of girls is increasingly being regarded not only as an assault on their physical integrity but also as an abusive practice and, as such, a human rights abuse.

The World Health Organization took a stand on the medicalization of FGM when, in 1982, it issued a statement that it should not be performed by health professionals under any circumstances. To date only one doctor has been disciplined for female genital mutilation: in 1993, in the United Kingdom, a doctor was struck off the medical register for professional misconduct for agreeing to perform genital mutilation.[17]

In the Netherlands in 1992 two medical anthropological researchers recommended that the government differentiate between the mutilating and non-mutilating forms of genital surgery and allow doctors to do ritual puncture of the clitoris.[18] However, at the symposium on FGM organized by the Netherlands Consultancy for Maternal Health and Family Planning in 1992,this policy was rejected by the government after wide protests and appeals from international organizations such as the WHO, feminists, women's organizations, human rights groups, and from African campaigners.

In a joint statement presented at the symposium by African participants, they stressed that 'because the girl child has no voice, governments should take all measures to guarantee protection to the girl child within their territory whatever their race, religion or political status'.[19] Calls for the medicalization of FGM by individuals have also come up in the UK,[20] and within the European Parliament.[21]

Age

The age at which the mutilations are carried out varies from area to area. It may be done at a few days old (for example, among the Ethiopian Jewish Falashas and the nomads of the Sudan), at

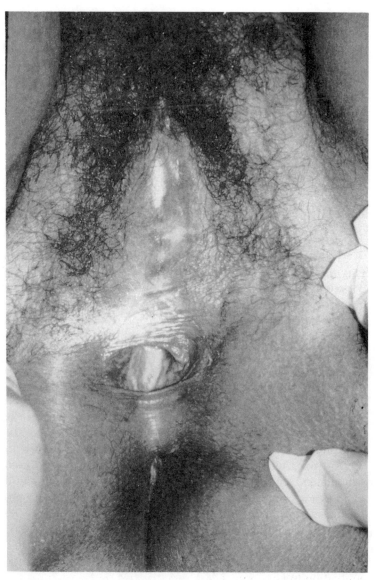

FIGURE 3
Extended infibulated vulva
FORWARD INTERNATIONAL

about seven years old (as in Egypt and many countries of central Africa) or in adolescence (among the Ibo of Nigeria, for instance, where excision takes place shortly before marriage, but only before the first child among the Aboh in midwestern Nigeria); or it may be carried out on widows, as reported among the Darasa ethnic group in Ethiopia.[22] FGM is so deeply rooted that in extreme cases where a woman who had escaped the practice had died, relatives might insist on the performance of FGM before burial could take place.[23, 24]

Female genital mutilation can also be performed on adult women in the following ways:

1 With their consent when marrying into different ethnic groups as has been noted, for example, among African women from southern Sudan who do not practise FGM when they marry northern Sudanese Arab men[25] and into different races.[26]

2 It can be used as a political tool by a dominant group on a minority and be forcibly imposed on adult women during periods of political unrest, as seen in some incidents in Kenya during the last general elections in 1993, for instance in the Mt Elgon area, where Sabaots warriors forcibly excised six Bukusu women, allegedly to scare away non-Kalenjins from voting.[27]

Most experts agree, however, that the age at which mutilation takes place is falling. For example, some refugees seeking asylum in the Western world have mutilated the girls at a younger age than usual, before coming to Europe, so as to overcome legislative pressures against FGM in these countries. In Australia, in 1993, two sisters, both under three years of age, were found infibulated. Another factor related to the practice of mutilation at an earlier age is that some older girls are resisting female genital mutilation. A case in point is Aminata Diop, a 23-year-old woman who fled her village in Mali and eventually sought asylum in France to avoid genital mutilation.[28] Below is a letter to a women's support group campaigning against female genital mutilation in London:

Dear Sir,
Please can you send me some information on female circumcision,
I am 16 years of age and my parents wish to send me to my Aun-
tie to have this done. They are very understanding but will not
explain what actually happens. I saw your address on Oracle.[29]

De-infibulation (opening up)

Women who are infibulated are meant to remain 'closed' until their marriage when one of their husband's roles is to 'open' them. Lantier tells of this in his description of the wedding in Somalia when the husband uses a dagger to open her:

'According to tradition, the husband should have prolonged and
repeated intercourse with her during eight days. This "work" is in
order to "make" an opening by preventing the scar from closing
again. During these eight days, the woman remains lying and
moves as little as possible in order to keep the wound open. The
morning after the wedding night, the husband puts his bloody
dagger on his shoulder and makes the rounds in order to obtain
general admiration.'[30]

PHYSICAL CONSEQUENCES

The health risks and complications of female genital mutilation depend upon the gravity of the mutilation, hygienic conditions, the skill and eyesight of the operator, and the struggles of the child. Whether immediate or long-term, they are grave.[31] Dr Mark Belsey of the Division of Family Health, World Health Organization, Geneva, remarked in a 1993 documentary inter-view, '...there is no single practice which has such a dramatic negative effect on health in the broadest sense as female genital mutilation.'[32]

Immediate complications

Short-term complications associated with female genital mutila-tion include: violent pain; haemorrhage from rupture of the blood vessels of the clitoris; post-operative shock (death can only be prevented if blood transfusion and emergency resuscitation are possible). The bad eyesight of the operator or the resistance of the child may cause damage to other organs: the urethra, the anal sphincter, vaginal walls or Bartholin's glands. Acute urine retention due to pain and fear of passing urine on the raw wound is common. Fractured clavicle, femur and humerus can result from heavy-handed restraint on the struggling child. As the instruments used have rarely been sterilized, tetanus (frequently fatal) and septicaemia often result.

HIV and hepatitis B can be transmitted through the use of nonsterile instruments, especially when genital mutilation is carried out simultaneously on groups of girls. The letter below, sent to Amnesty International, British Section, highlights the dangers of HIV transmission:

> *Dear Sir,*
> *With regard to your recent coverage of female circumcision, while in Malawi a couple of months ago I came across the story of a 14 year-old girl of the Yao tribe that inhabits land in the southern end of the country. She was diagnosed HIV-positive although she was a virgin. Blame was laid on the fact that during tribal circumcision the same razor would be used on any number of children at the same time. The solution the chief offered to take up was that in future each child was to bring their own razor.*[33]

Infibulation damages the sexual organs, and the reopening of the vulva after marriage damages them further. Both events increase the chance of infection, which in theory can increase the risk of infection by HIV. In some cases, where infibulation prevents vaginal intercourse, anal intercourse is used as an alternative; again, the resulting damage to tissue is a possible route of infection by HIV.

It is impossible to estimate the number of deaths caused by mutilation partly because the majority take place in rural areas where death records are not kept, and since the nature of the operation requires that unsuccessful attempts be concealed from strangers and health authorities, only a very small proportion of cases reach hospital. Nevertheless, hospital staff in all the areas concerned are very familiar with last-minute and often hopeless attempts to save bleeding, terrified little girls. Dr Rosemary Mburu, a Kenyan gynaecologist has estimated that 15 per cent of all circumcised females die of bleeding or infections;[34] other reports estimate that out of 1,000 females who undergo female genital mutilation 70 women die as a result.[35] Dr Mohamed Warsame, a Somali gynaecologist at Benadir Hospital, reported the death of a small girl from haemorrhage following infibulation, and 29 cases of bleeding following the procedure were seen at the hospital between 1984 and 1985.[36]

Those who perform mutilations are protected by the community. Invariably when death or infection result they are attributed to witchcraft and the 'evil eye', not to the excisors or to the fact that their instruments were nonsterile.

Long-term complications

Excision

The most common complication of excision is a lack of sensation during sexual intercourse due to the removal of the clitoral gland and the labia minora. Further narrowing of the vaginal opening can occur as a result of shrinkage of scar tissue formed following accidental cuts into the vaginal wall. This leads, first, to painful menstruation (dysmenorrhoea) as the menstrual blood cannot flow freely and, second, to painful intercourse. The most excruciating result of excision, rendering the whole genital area permanently and unbearably sensitive to touch, is the development of a neuroma, a tumour composed of nerve tissue, at the point of section of the dorsal nerve of the clitoris. Chronic vulval abscesses can also develop at the site where the clitoris is removed. Tears can occur during childbirth because scars in the clitoral zone open up, particularly if the baby is big. Where scarring is extensive, a fistula (an abnormal opening between the vagina and the bladder or between the vagina and the rectum) can occur due to obstructed labour. Primary vaginal stone,[37] vulval epidermoid cysts,[38] as well as maternal septicaemia (in parts of Nigeria excision is performed at the seventh month of pregnancy) resulting in death after excision,[39] have been reported in the medical literature.

Infibulation

Young infibulated girls are not able to empty their bladders fully if the opening left for urination is small. The backlog of urine leads to recurrent urinary and kidney infections and the formation of bladder stones.

Other grave complications include dysmenorrhoea since menstrual blood cannot escape freely, and young infibulated girls try to dislodge the accumulated clots with their fingernails, if the opening is big enough. Dr Ollivier, a military doctor in Djibouti, described the case of a 16-year-old girl brought to the hospital with unbearable abdominal pains. She had not menstruated for several months, and had not had intercourse, but her abdomen was swollen and sensitive, with the signs of a uterus in labour. She was infibulated, with a minuscule opening. Penetration would appear to have been impossible and there was no sign of beating of a foetal heart. Dr Ollivier performed a de-infibulation (opening of the scarred vulva), and released 3.4 litres of blackish foul-smelling blood.[40]

There are other accounts of similar complications, sometimes with tragic results: the increased size of the abdomen together with the absence of menstruation leads the family to think a girl is pregnant. She is therefore killed to preserve the 'honour' of the family.[41]

In England in 1989 the author was involved in a hospital case of a 15 year old infibulated girl with retained menstrual blood. The parents refused to sign consent forms for the doctor to open up the infibulation. A court order had to be issued to enable the doctor to de-infibulate and to let out four litres of putrid blood.[42]

Chronic infections of the uterus and vagina are frequent, the vagina having become a semi-sealed organ. Endometriosis and infertility are other problems associated with infibulation. Sometimes the collection of mucous secretions under the infibulation flap can lead to the growth of dermoid cysts as large as a grapefruit. Keloid scar formation on the vulval wound can become so enlarged as to obstruct walking.

Further complications during childbirth are unavoidable. Splitting of the scar is always needed to let the baby out. The tough obliterated vulva has lost its elasticity and, if it is not reopened in time, may fatally hold up the second stage of labour. The head of the baby may be pushed through the perineum, which tears more easily than the infibulation scar, so causing a high incidence of perineal tears. Recto-vaginal and vesico-vaginal fistulas (abnormal openings) are the unfortunate end results of prolonged obstructed labour and tears. There is unnecessary blood loss, and the pain produced may result in uterine inertia.The long and obstructed labour can lead to intrauterine foetal death, or brain damage to the baby. If a cut is made (bilateral or anterior episiotomy), other parts may be injured: the vagina or the cervix of the mother, or the scalp or any other part of the baby, especially if the midwife is working in a hurry. Again, there is the danger of infection.In some areas, custom may demand that a woman be reinfibulated, or sewn up again, after each delivery, and this may be done twelve times or more. At the beginning of her menopause, a woman is left with a mass of fibrous tissue at what used to be her vulval area. Incontinence after the menopause and prolapses of the vaginal wall are not uncommon.

Providing a comprehensive family planning service for women who are infibulated is difficult. Methods of contraception such as female barriers are likely to be precluded and inserting an IUD (intra-uterine device) is not easy. Vaginal examination and smear tests may not be possible.

Sexual health problems

This is an area which is very much neglected. The clitoral glans with its specific sensory apparatus is a primary erogenous zone. To understand the damage done to the clitoris, one needs to know what the clitoris is for and what it consists of.

THE CLITORAL SYSTEM
The clitoral glans is just the high point of a much larger clitoral structure. Leading to and from this glans, down round the entrance to the vagina and back again, is a network of clitoral nerves, muscles, glands, tissue and ligaments directly connected to it.[43]

Behind the clitoral tip (the equivalent of the tip of the penis)

FIGURE 4
Parting the lips of the vulva reveals the hood, or foreskin, of the clitoris

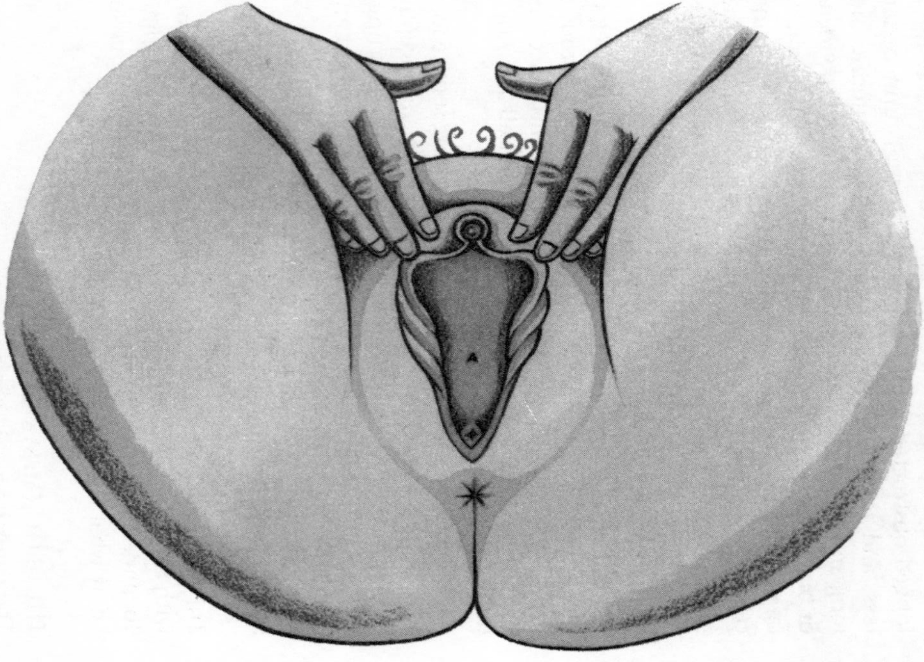

FIGURE 5
Clitoral 'legs', five or six centimetres long, follow the line of the pelvic bone

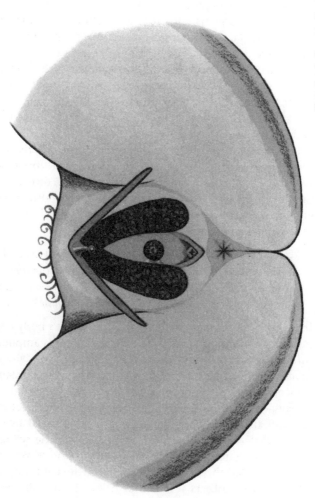

Illustrations by Fiona MacVicar/ The InkShed

is the clitoral 'stem' a couple of centimetres in length and leading down from it, wishbone fashion, are two clitoral 'legs', slen-
der ligaments 5 or 6 centimetres in length. These follow the line
of the pelvic bone and correspond to two very similar 'legs' or
'roots' within a penis. This whole structure forms a triangle with
the clitoral glans at the top, and the base formed by a transverse
muscle on the far side of the vagina. Within it are 'bulbs' of tissue which correspond to similar tissue inside the penis. During
arousal these fill with blood and the whole clitoral system swells
up or 'erects' until in terms of size it's roughly equivalent to an
erect penis, for all this is linked to other nerves and muscles in
and around both vagina and anus.[44]

Like the glans of the penis, the glans of the clitoris is the most
sensitive spot in the genital area and can focus sensation
received elsewhere. In both sexes it is pressure, direct or indirect,
on this organ which triggers orgasm, though both sexes experience the orgasm in other parts of their bodies too.[45]

The *Hite Report* explains the process:

> *'Clitoral stimulation evokes female orgasm, which takes place
> deeper in the body, around the vagina and other structures, just
> as stimulation of the tip of the male penis evokes male orgasm,
> which takes place inside the lower body of the male'*[46]

In all types of mutilation the part of a woman's body containing
nerves of vital importance to sexual enjoyment is amputated. The
earlier a woman is mutilated, the greater is the damage, since
infantile and adolescent masturbation teaches the organism and
the consciousness the proper function of sexual organs. There is
no surgical technique capable of repairing a clitoridectomy, or of
restoring the erogenous sensitivity of the amputated area.

Very little research has been conducted on the sexual experience of mutilated women. Some women who have undergone
genital mutilation are adamant that their sexuality has not been
affected, while others testify that it has. In the absence of any
comparison between sexual experience before and after clitoridectomy, it is difficult to know the real impact of the damage. It is claimed that female genital mutilation reduces the ease
with which sexual fulfilment in women is achieved.[47] Factors

such as the degree of mutilation, cultural and social expectations, affection and bonding in relationships, denial, are all vari-
ables which influence the sexuality of mutilated women. In 1967
Shandall discovered that of the sample of women he interviewed
in the Sudan, some had no idea at all of the existence of orgasm.
He reported on cases of tight infibulation where the husbands,
unable to penetrate into the vagina, resorted to anal intercourse,
or even used the urethral meatus as an opening.[48] On the other
hand, in 1989 Lightfoot-Klein talked with women in the Sudan,
who had experienced orgasm despite infibulation.[49]

Studies have been undertaken where men were questioned
about their sexual experience with women who have had genital
mutilation. Of 300 Sudanese husbands interviewed by Shandall
(each of whom had more than one wife, of whom only one was
infibulated), 266 stated categorically that they preferred non-
excised or *sunna*-circumcised women sexually. They enjoyed
intercourse with them more because they seemed to share with
them the desire, the act and the pleasure, he reports. Some
authors point to a link between female genital mutilation and
drug-taking in men, specifically the smoking of hashish in
Egypt.[50] Apparently these men experience difficulty in bringing
their women who have undergone excision to orgasm. To be
able to arouse these women and for them to experience pleasure,
men have to take drugs to help them hold their erections as long
as possible. Dr Mahran writes:

*'Excision is one of the causes of the ever increasing use of hashish
among men who believe, albeit wrongly, that smoking it delays
ejaculation, giving men their orgasms at the same time as their
excised wives: 16 per cent of excised women admit that their husbands smoke hashish for sexual reasons.'*[51]

The same link is observed between female genital mutilation and
narcotics in Yemen where the chewing of '*qat*' (a leaf with mild
amphetamine properties) is widespread.[52]

In a 1985 study, Badawi examined the effects of genital mutilation upon responses to sexual stimulation in a group of women
in Egypt.[53] Of these, 133 were genitally mutilated and 26 unmutilated. These women were compared with respect to sexual

excitement in response to stimulation of clitoris or clitoral area, stimulation of the labia areas and intercourse. Badawi found that 7.7 times as many unmutilated women experienced sexual excitement on stimulation of the clitoris/clitoral area than those of the genitally mutilated women. Masturbation (involving labia as well as clitoral areas) as the method of choice for sexual satisfaction was 2.2 times more frequent in unmutilated women. Manual stimulation of the clitoris/clitoral area resulted in orgasm in 50 per cent of the unexcised women and in 25 per cent of the genitally mutilated women.[54]

Badawi noted two findings from his survey. The first is that only 50 per cent of unmutilated women experienced orgasm with manual stimulation of the clitoris; and as many as 25 per cent of the genitally mutilated women were able to experience orgasm in response to stimulation of the clitoral area. Badawi concludes that the extent to which orgasmic potential in mutilated women is related to the nature and degree of genital mutilation is unknown, and is a subject worthy of future research.[55]

Many people see the removal of the hood of the clitoris (female circumcision) as a useless but harmless practice. The World Health Organization (WHO) in its recent classification of female genital mutilation does not include the removal of the hood of the clitoris.[56] However, reports from women who have undergone this procedure indicate the need to study this closely. The report from an Indian Daudi Bohra woman highlights this:

> 'My mother took me to the house of a woman in our Bohra mohalla district. Except for the lady, no one was at home. I was told to lie down on my back on the floor and spread my legs. It hurt me bad and brought tears to my eyes. The whole thing was over in a matter of minutes. As I grew up and became aware of my sexuality I realized the purpose of circumcision is to discourage masturbation. It limits the possibility of sexual pleasure from the stimulation of the clitoris. The circumcision exposes the nerve endings of the glans of the clitoris and for some women direct contact makes the area hypersensitive and painful to prolonged touch.'[57]

This is supported by reports of pain from some British women who have had cosmetic surgery to remove the hood of the clitoris to help them achieve orgasm and by those who have had reduction of the labia minora for cosmetic reasons.[58] In a 1992 study of Bedouin women in Israel who practise incision of the hood of the clitoris and the labia minora all women reported pain on intercourse in the months after marriage.[59]

Pain during intercourse is not an uncommon complaint for both excised and infibulated women. With infibulation, consummation of the marriage may take several weeks.[60] The opening of the scar of an infibulated woman is either made by the husband with his fingers, a razor, a knife or by a traditional midwife. In some communities husbands are expected to penetrate the minuscule opening with their penises. Below is a testimony of a Sudanese man's first sexual experience with his bride:

> 'The first experiences were very painful for her. For a long time we could not enjoy sex together, because it was a unilateral thing. It was I who had the orgasm. She only had fear and pain. I had had some experience, and knew either I would ruin the whole relationship, or with gentleness and patience I would eventually solve the problem. I loved her very much, and for a long time, for several months, we both tried very hard to make it work. It was a nightmare. Of course I wanted sex. Every time I approached her sexually, she bled. The wound I had caused was never able to heal. I felt horribly guilty. The whole thing was so abnormal. The thought that I was hurting someone I loved so dearly troubled me greatly. I felt like an animal. It is an experience that I would rather not remember. It was bad for both of us. It was not until after our first child was born that she could have relations without pain, and then she was able to enjoy sex for the first time. The child was born in England, and she was not resutured. I don't think I would permit that to be done to her again. Things are very good the way they are now, and we both enjoy sex together very much, now that nobody is suffering any pain.'[61]

Sexual dysfunction for both men and women relating to female genital mutilation can be a hidden problem which leads to disharmony and the break-up of marriages and relationships. Although elite women will seek de-infibulation in hospital prior to consummation, the majority do not have access to such services. Even when they are available, family pressure may prevent women from using them. The case of Amina, a 25-year old Somali refugee woman in London, illustrates this point:

> 'I was infibulated when I was nine years old. I have had four operations to open up the infibulation for sexual relations with my husband since I got married four years ago but all this has been unsuccessful. Each time my husband comes near me the place closes up. He cannot enter me. I have been through a lot of pain even to the point that I wanted to commit suicide. My husband unfortunately emotionally abuses me. He says I am a useless woman. It hurts me so much. I cannot speak about this to my family or to any members of the community. This will bring shame on my family. I need to see a psychologist but if my family or the community finds out that I am seeing a psychologist, there will be gossip in the community and I will be dismissed as a mad person.' [62]

Amina is suffering from post-traumatic stress which evokes severe vaginismus at intercourse. This is the result of the memories of pain she had suffered from female genital mutilation. Amina was able to see a doctor and a psycho-sexual counsellor because, luckily, she was in England, but in rural Africa such health care facilities dealing with women's sexual health needs as result of mutilation are nil.The number of women who suffer in silence and end up being dismissed by their communities as mad or outcasts is unknown.

PSYCHOLOGICAL CONSEQUENCES

Even less research has been done to date on the psychological aspects of these traditions. As a result of his work with Egyptian and Sudanese female patients, Dr T.A. Ba'asher, World Health Organization Regional Adviser for the Eastern Mediterranean on Mental Health, reports:

> 'It is quite obvious that the mere notion of surgical interference in the highly sensitive genital organs constitutes a serious threat to the child and that the painful operation is a source of major physical as well as psychological trauma.' [63]

Many personal accounts and research findings contain repeated references to anxiety prior to the operation, terror at the moment of being seized by an aunt or village matron, unbearable pain, the subsequent sense of humiliation and of being betrayed by parents, especially the mother. This is the story of Miami from the Gambia:

> '*At the age of 17, after she had completed her high school education, she was invited by her paternal aunt to spend her holidays with her cousin. According to Miami those were the worst holidays she had spent. One week after her holiday began, she was informed that she and her cousins were to attend a ceremony for mature girls. No further explanations were given. On arrival at the supposed ceremonial venue, they were taken to a big house, beautifully decorated. Miami noticed that soon after they entered the compound the gates were securely locked up and the house was later locked up too...No sooner did Miami enter the house when all the women grabbed her and stripped her. At first she thought she was going to be slaughtered like a sheep during Ramadan as she was thrown to the ground and her hands and her legs were being tied up. "I thought I was going to be the lamb of sacrifice for the ceremony," she said. Her first reaction was to scream as her mouth was the only movable part of her body by then. The women were quick to react; a large buttock was resting on her face.*' [64]

On the other hand, there are references to special clothes and good food associated with the event, to the pride felt in being like everyone else, in being 'made clean', in having suffered without screaming. Clearly, if in a community sufficient pressure is put on a child to believe that her clitoris or genitals are dirty, dangerous or a source of irresistible temptation, she will feel relieved psychologically to be made like everyone else. To be different produces anxiety and mental conflict. An unexcised, non-infibulated girl is despised and made the target of ridicule, and no one in her community will marry her. Thus what is clearly understood to be her life's work, namely marriage and childbearing, is denied her. So, in tight-knit village societies where mutilation is the rule, it will be the exception who will suffer psychologically, unless she has another very strong identity to substitute for the community identity which she has lost.[65]

There is no doubt that genital mutilation will have overwhelming psychological effects on an unmotivated girl, unsupported by her family, village, peers and community. The story of Amina from Somalia, who was infibulated in Abu Dhabi, illustrates this.

> *'I was eight when it was done. I still feel hurt and aggrieved*
> *about it like there is something missing and I am not a real*
> *girl...My aunt, her sister, my mother and some neighbours held*
> *me down...and they didn't give me an anaesthetic.'*[66]

Amina is 22 now and is still grieving about what happened to her. She finds it difficult to keep a fulfilling relationship because of pain and inability to feel any sensation during intercourse. Most of the time when she has intercourse she feels she is being used, which makes her go through periods of very severe depression.[67]

There are women suffering silently over sexual health problems. The impact on their psychological health has not been studied nor do we know about the extent of the problem. Women are not able to discuss their problems freely because of social taboos and because of fear of being branded as promiscuous or as prostitutes. Dr Nahid Toubia observed this among her female patients in the outpatient department of the gynaecology clinic in the Sudan:

> *'Thousands of women present themselves with vague complaints*
> *all metaphorically linked to their pelvises, which really means*
> *their genitals since they are socially too shy to speak of their geni-*
> *tals. They complain of symptoms of anxiety and depression, loss*
> *of sleep, backache and many other complaints uttered in sad*
> *monotonous voices. When I probe them a little, the flood of their*
> *pain and anxiety over their genitals, their sexual lives, their fertil-*
> *ity and all the other physical and psychological complications of*
> *their circumcision is unbearable. These women are holding back*
> *a silent scream so strong, if uttered, it would shake the earth.*
> *Instead it is held back depleting their energy and draining their*

*confidence in their abilities. Meanwhile the medical establish-
ment treats them as malingerers and a burden on the health system and its resources.*[68]

Suppressed pain can sometimes resurface when faced with graphic pictures of actual mutilation. This is shown in the experience of Guenet, a 40-year-old Eritrean living in the US. She had been excised in Eritrea when she was five years old. Not long ago she saw a documentary on female genital mutilation which brought all the pain that she had been going through to a head. The mutilation that she had suffered in childhood had damaged some nerves and she had been in constant pain ever since. She decided to contact other women who had undergone genital mutilation and organized a private meeting. She reassured them that the mutilation they had been through was not their fault. It was all right for them to speak out. For two hours the women sat and cried, some rocking in their chairs.[69]

There is a lot of work to be done, for women's health care in Africa only deals with family planning, pregnancy and childbirth. Sexual health and mental health are areas that should be looked into in the future.

2

THE PRACTICE

'Women are victims of outdated customs, attitudes and male prejudice. This results in negative attitudes of women about themselves. There are many forms of sexual oppression, but this particular one is based on the manipulation of women's sexuality in order to assure male domination and exploitation. The origins of such practices may be found in the family, society and religion.'

Raqiya Haji Dualeh Abdalla[1]

REPRESSION OF FEMALE SEXUALITY ACROSS CULTURES

To those from other cultures unfamiliar with the practice of female genital mutilation, it may appear shocking, horrifying and even barbaric; yet it is important that it is not viewed as an isolated practice. Female genital mutilation is part of a continuum of patriarchal repression of female sexuality, which has been repressed in a variety of ways in all parts of the world throughout history and up to the present time. Methods vary in scope and in degree, but not in kind. Female slaves in ancient Rome had one or more rings put through their labia majora to prevent them having intercourse. Chastity belts were brought to Europe by the Crusaders during the twelfth century and used to ensure that women, locked up in these iron contraptions, remained faithful while their husbands were away fighting. In Russia, the Skoptozy (meaning 'the circumcisers'), a Christian sect, were reported to practise infibulation to ensure perpetual virginity. They justified this practice with a quote from the St Matthew's Gospel (chapter 19, verse 12) which states, '...and there be eunuchs, which have made themselves eunuchs for the kingdom of heaven's sake'.[2]

Going back in women's history to find FGM practised outside Africa was quite revealing. Robin Morgan and Gloria Steinem provide interesting insights into the way in which FGM manifested itself in North America and in Europe.[3] According to Morgan and Steinem, Sigmund Freud, the renowned psychologist, performed psychic clitoridectomies on all females in North America and in Europe for more than a century. He decreed that a 'vaginal' orgasm was a mark of maturity (even though it does not physiologically exist) and that clitoral orgasm must be abandoned (even though orgasm begins in the clitoral nerves). This propaganda had negative effects on the psyche and the sexuality of millions of women in North America and in Europe.

In the nineteenth century, medical texts also proclaimed genital mutilation as an accepted treatment for 'nymphomania', 'hysteria', 'masturbation', 'deviance' and other non-conforming behaviour.[4] In London, Dr Isaac Baker Brown justified scissoring off the clitoris of some of his patients as a cure for various ailments such as insomnia, sterility and 'unhappy' marriages.[5] In 1859 Dr Charles Meigs recommended the application of silver solution to the clitoris of female children who masturbated.[6] And until 1925 in the United States, a medical association called the Orificial Surgery Society offered training in clitoridectomy and infibulation '...because of the vast amount of sickness and suffering which could be saved the gentler sex'. Such mutilations occurred as recently as the 1940s and 1950s in the United States. For example, in New York, the daughter of a well-to-do family underwent clitoridectomy as 'treatment' for masturbation, as recommended by a family physician.[7] Some prostitutes were encouraged by well-meaning Church social workers to have this procedure as a form of 'rehabilitation'.[8]

It must not be thought that such practices have been eradicated. Indeed there are women living in North America and Europe today who have suffered this form (as well as other, more familiar, forms) of gynophobic, medically unnecessary, mutilating surgery.[9] The author has met five British women in their 40s and over who have had clitoridectomies performed on them in child-hood for non-physical reasons. Because of persuasion by their partners that their labia minora are ugly, some white British women have gone for labia reduction purely for aesthetic rea-sons. This, and hymen repair to restore 'virginity' for Arab and Asian girls costs some £1,500 in private clinics in London.[10] Equally, in Japan, demands by men for proof of virginity from their brides have reached such proportions that women are pre-pared to pay up 500,000 yen (£3,000) for hymen repair.[11]

Whatever the justifications, mechanisms and pressures imposed on women to make their bodies conform to societal expectations, we can explore the real reasons for them only within the context of patriarchy.

In no other continent did the mutilation of female sexual organs take such hold as Africa. We will look at its prevalence today in Africa, the Middle East, Asia and South America, and explore the origins and the reasons given for the practice.

Prevalence of FGM

At present it is estimated that over 100 million girls and women in Africa alone are genitally mutilated.[12,13] At the current rate of population growth in Africa, two million girls a year — some 6,000 per day — are estimated by some authors to be at risk of FGM.[14] However, information available on total prevalence and rates by type of operation is incomplete. It is often based on anecdotal reports or biased samples using unclear or faulty meth-ods of data collection.[15] The only country with reliable nation-wide data on FGM is the Sudan, where three surveys included data on FGM.[16,17]

One or more forms of FGM are reported to be practised in more than 28 African countries, although national borders are not so important as ethnic groups practising FGM straddle boundaries (see map on page viii). Because civil wars have caused major refugee movements from the Horn of Africa, FGM is now being performed in refugee camps. It is therefore more accurate to view female genital mutilation as being practised by specific ethnic groups in Africa.[18] The gravity of mutilations varies from one ethnic group to another. Those close together geographically are by no means affected in the same way: for example, in Kenya, the Kikuyu practise excision and the Luo do not; in Nigeria, the Yoruba, the Ibo and the Hausa do, but not the Nupes or the Fulanis; in Senegal, the Woloff do not practise mutilation. There are many such examples. There are three countries where almost all the female population undergo FGM. These are Somalia, Djibouti and north and central Sudan where more than 80 per cent of women have undergone the more severe mutilation, infibulation.

Outside Africa, FGM is practised in Oman, both North and South of Yemen, and the United Arab Emirates (UAE). Other Arab countries in which it has been reported to be practised are Bahrain, Qatar and some areas of Saudi Arabia.[19] Reports from doctors and midwives working in the Middle East indicate that infibulation is practised widely by immigrants from the Sudan and Somalia.[20] However, the extent of the practice in the Middle East is unknown and research data is required to confirm its prevalence and type. FGM is practised by the Ethiopian Jewish Falashas who have recently settled in Israel and there are reports that the Bedouin women of Israel also practise FGM.[21,22]

Clitoridectomy is reported to be practised in South America by some indigenous people in Peru,[23] Colombia,[24] Mexico and Brazil.[25] Again the extent of the practice is unknown. Female circumcision is practised by the Muslim populations of Indonesia and Malaysia and by Bohra Muslims in India, Pakistan and East Africa.

In Western countries – Europe, Australia, Canada and the USA – immigrant women from areas where FGM is practised are reported to be genitally mutilated,[26] but there are no studies on its prevalence in immigrant populations nor on the numbers of girls at risk.

ORIGINS OF FGM

The customs and beliefs surrounding the various forms of FGM are so widespread and so tenacious that far more research needs to be done on their origins and past and present practices.

Marie Assaad feels that there is sufficient evidence to assume that infibulation was practised in ancient Egypt, and that it was perhaps there that the custom originated.[27] An alternative explanation is that it could have been an old African rite that came to Egypt by diffusion (infibulation is known in the Sudan as 'pharaonic circumcision' and in Egypt it is referred to as 'Sudanese circumcision'). It is interesting to note that the most radical form of FGM, infibulation, is most widespread in northern and central Sudan, Somalia and Djibouti, areas where Arab and Black African cultures met. It is reported that infibulation, a chastity belt made of flesh, was enforced on black African women in these areas in the ancient Arab slave trade.[28] The dominant culture in these areas is Arabic and, to this day, African women from southern Sudan (where FGM is not practised) who have married into the dominant group — Sudanese Arabs in northern Sudan — have had to undergo infibulation. It is possible that over a period of time infibulation as practised in northeastern Africa became a mark of distinction as it was the mark of entry of Black Africans into the dominant ancient Arab group.

James DeMeo believes that the global distribution of both male and female genital mutilations among non-Western people suggests their genesis in the deserts of north-east Africa and the Near East. The practice was transmitted from one region to the other by virtue of relocation diffusion, and by phases of military conquests of cultures who do not mutilate by invading cultures which do, or by 'voluntary adoption' of those assimilated cultures.[29] He noted also that in sub-Saharan Africa and Oceania genital mutilations were practised independently prior to the Islamic period, notably among warrior-like people.[30] In Indonesia, Professor Pratiknya reports that female circumcision has been known since the eighth century, when Islam was brought there.[31]

In conclusion, it seems likely that genital mutilations were introduced when the Nile Valley was invaded by militant pastoral nomads, and culturally transformed, around 3100 BC.[32] These invaders, who possessed Asian and Semitic characteristics, ushered in an era of divine kings, ritual widow murder, a military and priestly caste and other trappings of extreme patriarchal authoritarian culture.[33] Although female genital mutilation occurs in Egypt today, there is no evidence of it in the Ptolemaic or earlier periods.[34] Female genital mutilation must have developed independently amongst certain ethnic groups in sub-Saharan Africa as part of puberty rites.

MOTIVES FOR AND FUNCTIONS OF FGM

The justifications for female genital mutilations are at first glance bewildering, often conflicting, and always at odds with biological fact. They are worth examining in detail simply because they are believed in, and with such tenacity. The question then remains as to why they are believed in.

Generally, the reasons given, as they appear in research papers, interviews and testimonials, fall into four groups: psycho-sexual, religious, sociological and hygienic.

Psycho-sexual

Beliefs surrounding FGM often run very deep and may appear to many people outside that particular belief system to be irrational. For example, African animist beliefs surrounding FGM have been dismissed simplistically as mere superstitions, whereas deeper analysis points to a complex set of ideas which underpins a social system.

The Mossi of Burkina Faso, the Bambara and the Dogon in Mali believe that the clitoris would be dangerous during childbirth when contact with the baby's head would cause its death.[35] In some areas, notably Ethiopia, people believe that if the female genitals are not excised, they will grow and dangle between the legs like a man's. Consequently women are frightened into doing away with their sexual organ, created solely for sexual pleasure, in the same way that Freud used propaganda through psychology to influence women to abandon clitoral orgasm. From these myths it can be seen that the clitoris is viewed as a 'rival to the male sexual organ and is, as such, intolerable to men'.[36] Among the Bambara this is expressed in its extreme form by the belief that, upon entering an unexcised woman, a man could be killed by the secretion of a poison from the clitoris at the moment of contact with the penis.[37]

Another deeply held belief among the Dogon and the Bambara in Mali is that both the female and the male sex exist within each person at birth. The clitoris (representing the masculine element in a young girl), and the foreskin (representing femininity in a boy), must both be excised to demarcate clearly the sex of the person.[38] This obviously expresses the fear of an initially hermaphroditic human nature and of women's sexuality.[39]

In other instances society is quite direct about curtailing women's sexuality. Very frequently, the reason offered by both women and men for mutilation is 'the attenuation of sexual desire'. Since the focus of this desire is clearly recognized to be the clitoris, excision is believed to protect a woman against her oversexed nature, saving her from temptation, suspicion and disgrace, while preserving her chastity.

These beliefs must be understood in the context of societies where female virginity is an absolute prerequisite for marriage, and where an extramarital relationship provokes the most severe penalties. So strong is the association of mutilation with premarital chastity that in many areas a non-excised girl is ridiculed and often forced to leave her community and, regardless of her virginity, will stand little or no chance of marriage.

In societies where a man has several wives, it is said that since it is physically impossible for him to satisfy them all, it helps if they are not too sexually demanding. It also supposedly reduces the chance of women straying.

The Tagouna of the Ivory Coast believe that a non-excised woman cannot conceive, whereas the Yoruba use excision as a form of contraception. They believe that sperm finds its way into a nursing mother's milk with adverse effects for the child. Thus women were expected to live without sex for eighteen months while breast-feeding, and the fact of having undergone genital mutilation made it easier for them to bear a sexless life.[41]

Although the intention of the operation may be to diminish a woman's desire, the facts, from a medical point of view, are that excision of the clitoris reduces sensitivity, but it cannot reduce desire, which is a psychological attribute. Desire is as keenly felt, but achieving orgasm is very difficult.

Offering as a reason for infibulation 'the preservation of virginity and the prevention of immorality' is odd on a strictly practical level, since a re-infibulation can easily be made to look like the original one. Thus infibulation can be construed as giving a girl more chances to 'misbehave'.[42] Cases are reported from Somalia, where most husbands are polygamous and where divorce is cheap, of women paid for, married, divorced, reinfibulated, paid for and married again five times or more.

In the course of his research in the Sudan, Dr A.A. Shandall examined 200 prostitutes, of whom 170 had been infibulated, a rate higher than among a control group of hospital patients. He concludes:

'Infibulation does not confer any protection or deterrent action on females. Moreover, the vulval skin diaphragm, being an artificially constructed device, can always be reconstructed without any suspicion that this is not the original infibulation. In the writer's opinion, infibulation would encourage immorality rather than protect against it.'[43]

However, he failed to appreciate the fact that prostitutes do not generally work for pleasure but for economic survival. Of course excision is not a barrier to penetrative intercourse. However frustration in not being able to achieve full sexual pleasure might provoke promiscuity. In such situations the woman is never satisfied during sexual intercourse; she may seek several partners in an attempt to find satisfaction.

Religious

Excision and infibulation are practised by followers of a number of different religions such as Muslims, Catholics, Protestants, Copts, Animists, and non-believers in the various countries concerned. As will be seen, however, there is no basis in the various religious texts for FGM but rather it is how these religious books have been interpreted to the people that matters.

ISLAM
Female genital mutilation is not mentioned in the Koran, although it has frequently been carried out by some Muslim

communities in the genuine belief that it was demanded by the Islamic faith. How did this happen and what is the position of Islam on the excision of girls?

According to Dr Aldeeb Abu-Sahlieh (1994), Muslim law, which governs the lives of all believers, emanates from two sources; the Koran and the anthology of *sunna* (tradition which is words and actions) of the Prophet Mohammed, to which should be added *igtihad*, tenets of the school of Muslim law through the centuries.[44] The *fatwas*, the opinions of Muslim religious scholars, come under *igtihad*. The *fatwas* are not legally binding but are morally obligatory for the believer.

Under the anthology of the *sunna* there are three sayings of the Prophet Mohammed relating to female circumcision. While there is unanimous agreement among Muslim religious leaders and scholars that infibulation is forbidden in Islam, their interpretations and positions regarding the excision of girls remain ambiguous. Sheikh Dr Abdel Rahman Al Nagger,a religious scholar from Sudan, explains the position of the different scholars and sects as follows:

1. The scholars of the Shafeite sect believe that both circumcision of males and excision of females are obligatory.
2. The scholars and jurists of the Hanifite and Malikite sects believe that circumcision of males is *sunna* (an act practised by the Prophet Ibrahim) and that excision of females is preferable.
3. The scholars of the Hanbelite sect believe that circumcision is a mandatory obligation for males and a good deed for girls.
4. The belief of modern contemporary scholars may be summed up in the words of Sheikh Mahmoud Shaltout, former Sheikh of Al Azhar in Cairo, the most famous university of the Islamic world, who stated:

'Islamic legislation provides a general principle, namely that should meticulous and careful examination of certain issues prove that it is definitely harmful or immoral, then it should be legitimately stopped to put an end to this damage or immorality. Therefore, since the harm of excision has been established, excision of the clitoris of females is not mandatory obligation, nor is it a sunna.*'*[45]

According to Abu-Sahlieh, although the 1949 *fatwa* from the Egyptian Fatwa Committee declared that abandoning excision does not constitute a sin, there have been two more *fatwas* since which are rigid in their position on FGM.[46] The latest, dated 29 January 1981 and issued by the present Great Sheikh of Al Azhar, opposed giving up excision. He insists that it is impossible to abandon the lessons of the Prophet Mohammed in favour of the teaching of others, such as doctors, because medical science evolves and does not remain constant. According to him the responsibility for excision lies with parents and with those responsible for the girl's welfare. Those who avoid it are not carrying out their duty.[47]

Given these conflicting opinions, it is not surprising that Muslims believe strongly in the practice. Without a firm stand by religious leaders, forbidding it, it will be difficult to convince believers of the sects which promote excision. One positive development is the shift from infibulation to excision, as a result of a consensus among religious leaders that FGM not carried out according to the *sunna* is forbidden. However, they have not specified what the *sunna* entails: for some it is the removal of the top end of the clitoris and for others it involves the whole clitoris and labia minora.

CHRISTIANITY

Female genital mutilation is not mentioned in the Bible but it is practised by some Christians from all denominations. In the seventeenth century, Roman Catholic missionaries in Ethiopia attempted to discourage FGM among their converts but quickly found that they were losing their believers. They sought advice from Rome. According to Fran Hosken, in the eighteenth century the Papacy of the Roman Catholic Church officially supported genital mutilation after a medical mission was sent from Rome to Ethiopia to confirm whether Ethiopian women suffer from hypertrophy of the clitoris.[48] In Kenya it is reported that while the Scottish Presbyterian and Anglican Churches were trying to stop FGM in the 1920s and were excommunicating those followers who mutilated their girls, the Roman Catholic Church did not condemn it.[49] A keen member of the Roman Catholic

Church had this to say about the position it took at the time:

'The Roman Catholic Church does not mind whether girls are circumcised or not, Christians who circumcise girls are not excommunicated'.[50]

Clearly, the Roman Catholic Church did not want to lose its converts. In Kenya, the Protestant missionaries' attempts to stop FGM met with resistance and it became a political issue. In *Facing Mount Kenya*,[51] written in the 1930s, the late President Jomo Kenyatta, a Kikuyu, wrote that no proper Kikuyu would dream of marrying a girl who had not been circumcised. However, it was a position that his successor, President Arap Moi, from the Luo ethnic group which does not practise female genital mutilation, abandoned. In 1982 he declared a ban on female genital mutilation in Kenya.

The most active Christian Church in Africa campaigning against female genital mutilation is the Coptic Orthodox Church in Egypt.

In conclusion, it is quite clear that FGM has no strong basis in either Islam or Christianity but religion is interpreted by chauvinistic religious leaders to endorse the subjugation of women. For change to happen, the participation of female religious scholars in the reinterpretation of religion is crucial.

Sociological

Some scholars explain the practice in terms of initiation rites, of development into adulthood. In many areas (in northern Sudan, among the Kikuyu in Kenya, the Tagouna in the Ivory Coast, and the Bambara in Mali) an elaborate ceremony surrounded, and in some cases still surrounds, the event. There are special songs, dances and chants intended to teach the young girl her duties and the desirable characteristics of a good wife and mother. The event is rich in ritual and symbolism, with special convalescent huts for the girls attended only by the instructress, where the girls are isolated from the rest of society until they emerge, healed, as marriageable women or, in the case of very young girls, with gifts of special clothes and food.

However, it seems that today in many of these societies the

ceremonial aspects are falling away, and with both excision and infibulation being performed at a young age, they cannot be construed as having anything to do with entry into adulthood or marriage. Nor does the child's role in society change at all after the mutilation, undermining the hypothesis that it is an initiation rite.

Assitan Diallo devoted her thesis, entitled *L'Excision en milieu Bambara,*[52] to discovering whether excision possesses the same functional value in Mali today as it did in the past and whether it still has its initiation significance. She delved deeply into the details of ritual ceremonies, and discovered from her respondents (who were women, excised some time ago, and men, considering the excision of their children today) that these ceremonies have disappeared. The traditional songs are no longer taught to the girls, and not one of her respondents had received any instruction concerned with initiation to adulthood.

African women are beginning to question the content of what used to be initiation rites.[53] They believe that it is in these initiation rites that the patriarchal ideology is reinforced through 'songs, loaded speeches, and actions throughout the period of stay in the initiation chamber'.[54]

HYGIENE AND AESTHETICS

In some African countries where FGM is practiced — Egypt, Sudan, Somalia, Ethiopia — the external female genitals are considered dirty. In Egypt, for instance, the unexcised girl is called *nigsa* (unclean) and bodily hairs are removed in an effort to attain a smooth and, therefore, clean body. The same sentiment appears in Somalia and Sudan where the aim of infibulation is to produce a smooth skin surface, and women questioned insisted that it made them cleaner.

Yet in practice infibulation clearly has the effect opposite to that of promoting hygiene: urine and menstrual blood cannot escape naturally resulting in discomfort, odour and infection. Similarly, it is sometimes considered that female genitals are ugly or disfiguring in their natural state. However, the idea of female and male genitals being dirty or ugly is not confined to those who practice female genital multilation. It is the responses and practices arising from these deeply held beliefs which are different in the case of FGM.

Conclusion

It is clear that repression of female sexuality cuts across cultures, manifesting itself through various ideological media. Psychology and patriarchal myths are both used to control girls and women's sexuality. Another medium used to reinforce societal views on female sexuality is the puberty rite. Religion is central to the lives of many women and this, too, can be manipulated to control their sexuality.

3

WHAT ARE THE ISSUES?

'In defending women and in appealing to them to fulfil them-
selves, we say that women should not rely on men and should
not expect condescension from them. The development and the
liberation of women of our country, the women of Africa, of
women as a whole, will not come about as an act of charity. It
will depend on their will and their determination to struggle and,
therefore, their grasp of the social contradictions that oppose
women and men.'

Captain Thomas Sankara, late President of Burkina Faso.[1]

Why do mothers submit their daughters to genital mutilation if they as women have suffered it? There are no easy explanations but exploring their position within the family and in society as a whole will shed light on the reason why women collude in the mutilation of their daughters.

THE POSITION OF WOMEN IN SOCIETY

There is an obvious danger in generalizing about the position of women within the societies which practise female genital mutilation because of the diversity of history and cultures in which it occurs. The stereotypical images of African women oscillate between strong independent women, for example, the market women in West Africa, to very oppressed women, for example, mixed Arab/African women from the north-east and the Horn of

Africa. It is not uncommon for people to support these images by citing historical black warrior queens, female chiefs and 'queen mothers', women holding key positions in governmental services and in religion. The realities of life for a large majority of women are quite different.

There are certainly vestiges of female-orientated societies in Africa and it is important that, when talking about African women, distinctions are made between matrilineal and patrilineal societies. Some of the very few matrilineal societies existing in the world today are in Africa. In those societies, where descent is reckoned in the female line, women tend to have more rights and freedoms than they do in patrilineal communities. In matrilineal Akan society in southern Ghana, for example, girls are highly valued and, because of the lineage structure, a woman's children always belong to her. When an Akan woman marries she retains a considerable amount of independence: she is not obliged to move into her husband's household with its extended family; she can continue to rely on support from her mother's side of her family; in the traditional agricultural communities, she has access to land to farm through her mother's side of the family as well as through her husband's; she is not restricted in her movements and can sell the surplus of her produce and keep the profit.

The first menstruation is celebrated, as it is a sign of fertility and thus continuation of the lineage. The rites of passage for adolescent girls moving into womanhood do not include female genital mutilation. Girls are declared marriageable after the rites of passage. In such societies the bride price was just a token and nothing on the scale seen in recent times or among patrilineal groups. The natural sexuality of women is regarded as normal and even today women can get a divorce for sexual dissatisfaction. There is no cult of virginity and chastity. Having sex with girls before they have celebrated the rites of passage is taboo. A resulting pregnancy is viewed as polluting for the whole community, which has to perform certain rituals to purify itself and may banish the guilty couple forever. This was once the major deterrent against premarital sex, although today outside influences and rapid social change have reduced its effectiveness. However, matriliny is not to be confused with matriarchy, as the overall power in these societies still lies with men. Matriliny is dying out as its ethos conflicts with the patriarchy of the modern capitalist economy. Women are the main losers in the process.

The vast majority of African women, however, do not come from matrilineal societies. They are neither queens nor do they hold key jobs in modern government. The silent majority of African women are illiterate, poor rural women, whose lives are still governed by overt patriarchy with built-in complex social mechanisms to control their sexuality and reproductive capacity. The position of women in both Black and Arab Africa is influenced by many factors: their class position and affiliation, educational level and individual consciousness about their rights, economic independence, religious and cultural influences.

THE FAMILY

The common thread running through all the ethnic groups in Africa practising FGM is that they are patrilineal-based societies. In other words, these cultures are male-dominated societies where resources and power are generally under male control.

> *'Patriarchy is based upon the principle of the dominance of the father over the mother with respect to the parentage of children and by extension, the primacy of the male in human society, which implies the subordination of the female. Furthermore paternity itself can only be established with any degree of certainty in individual cases by the very strict control of the females that men mate with, in the absence of which only maternity is sure. Thus the only way in which a father can establish his fatherhood is by firstly ensuring that his mate has no relationship with any other man, and then by recognizing the offspring as his own by a process of adoption and naming'.*[1]

Even within these male dominated societies it is inaccurate to paint a picture of the all-encompassing subjugation of women and to make generalizations. It is important to stress that women enjoy a certain degree of licence within socially prescribed roles and areas of life, and that even in oppressive situations you will find extremely strong women who defy all kinds of assumptions.

The ideological underpinnings of FGM have already been discussed. The main point to stress is that the practice of FGM is not presented to women in a straightforward manner; it has been shrouded in mystery, magic and fear. Women receive social approval when they undergo FGM and gain certain benefits: being marriageable and thus having access to resources in the community. The concept of becoming a 'woman' and being elevated to a higher status after undergoing genital mutilation is a theme which runs through all the communities practising FGM. Because of the social approval, and the sanctions women face if they do not undergo FGM, they inevitably end up viewing it in a positive light.

In rural Africa there is a high rate of illiteracy among women and this compounds their powerlessness. Nor do they have access to broader health education. This lack of scientifically based knowledge contributes to the continuation of female genital mutilation. For example,women are told that the clitoris will endanger the life of their unborn baby. These are areas with high infant mortality so consequently they promote FGM as a prerequisite for the good health of their children. Similarly, women are told that their fertility will be adversely affected if they do not undergo FGM. Barrenness is the worst fate to befall women in traditional society so they perpetuate the practice in an effort to protect their children and to facilitate fertility and fecundity.

Despite various regional and cultural differences, the family form which is most common in rural areas is the extended family system, where several generations of the family live together. This usually includes the patriarch, the father, who is the head of the family and is revered. Others may be wives, grandmothers and great aunts, sons and their wives and children, unmarried children and so on. In the absence of the father the eldest son will take up his role. The nuclear family unit where a man, his wife and children live alone in one house is an urban phenomenon favoured by an urban elite.

The extended family has close ties and members are very supportive of each other. In the absence of state social security (income for the unemployed, free health care, care of the elderly, pensions, etc.) the extended family serves as the social security for all the members of the family. Women receive support within the family, for example with child care, but it is also within the family unit that the oppression of women is most acutely felt. This is explained under the next section on marriage.

One cannot discuss FGM without explaining the concept of family *honour* which prevails strongly in the Middle East and some of the areas where female genital mutilation is practised: northern Sudan,Djibouti, Egypt and the Horn of Africa. Honour is a collective property of the family. If one person loses her honour the entire family is dishonoured. While honour generally derives from male acts and attributes, both men and women can be a source of dishonour. The most dishonourable experience for a man is the sexual impropriety of a female member of the family, and it is his responsibility to mete out the severe punishment it incurs. Once a woman's honour is lost it cannot be restored. Coupled with a belief that women who have not undergone genital mutilation are filled with an uncontrollable sexual energy, this means that women will naturally be obsessed with chastity and virginity, which are seen as only sustainable through the practice of FGM.

Economic survival, marriage and FGM

In many communities women's access to land and to economic resources is through the male members of the family and husbands, which implies that they cannot directly inherit land or be in control of major resources. In communities with a subsistence economy the introduction of cash crops has meant that women play the role of producers and men overseers, middlemen and distributors, roles which have been viewed by some development experts as the key to the exploitation of women by men.

As we have seen, the practice of female genital mutilation is strongly linked to virginity, chastity and fidelity which are prerequisites for marriage. A bride price cannot be obtained if the bride is not 'pure'. For example, in Nigeria the operation serves the purpose of enabling the potential mother-in-law to discover whether the girl is a virgin or not: if she is found not to be a virgin, the husband-to-be has the right to reject her and refuse to go along with the marriage. A row probably ensues and a refund of the dowry has to be made. The disgraced family is stigmatized, and the girl may have to leave home to find a husband outside her community.[3]

A young Somali woman describes what commonly occurs on the day of the wedding:

'Women from the groom's family visit and examine the bride. They check to ensure that infibulation has been done and that she is a virgin. The genital area should be as smooth as the palm of one's hand. To make intercourse easier, the vulva may be cut open slightly. Otherwise, the groom widens the opening with his penis which is painful for both the bride and groom.'[4]

On the wedding night, a cloth is placed under the bride's genital area. After intercourse, the cloth is displayed to the members of the groom's family as proof of the bride's virginity. Having too large an opening can be grounds for divorce. If the groom refers to the sexual experience as 'falling into a ditch' he may annul the marriage the next day.[5]

Early and arranged marriages are other forms of restrictive practices which compound many of the problems faced by young girls and, later, adult women. Young women do not have a choice over whom they marry. Marriages are contracted not only for procreation but for the purpose of forging alliances between families (e.g. to enhance the social and economic status of the family). The marital union is often regularized by the exchange of gifts and payments in kind by the husband-to-be's family to the bride-to-be's family, the amount varying from one ethnic group to another. In nomadic communities this exchange could be as large as a herd of cattle or camels.

Two explanations have been put forward for the transfer of these gifts or goods. The first, favoured by cultural nationalists and anthropologists, is that the transfer of these goods is symbolic of the transfer of rights which places obligation on two people in the performance of certain duties, these rights forming the legal basis of the marriage. The second interpretation, favoured by African feminists, is that the transfer of goods or property is a way of moving goods around in society to strengthen alliances between families and clans. Women are merely pawns in the transaction; their rights as persons to determine their destinies are considered irrelevant to the total functioning of the family and society as large. Hence the restrictions and controls over their lives, their reproductive capacity and, particularly, their sexuality. A woman's status is elevated in marriage, especially as the bearer of sons for the purposes of inheritance. In recent times, however, African feminists have started to question the bride price as a human rights issue and have called for its abolition.[6]

One advantage of marital contracts based on strengthening alliances between families is that it becomes in the interest of the two families to make sure that the marriage works. However, the goods transfer could be interpreted by husbands, and by members of the extended family, as tantamount to buying a woman. The bride's family could be motivated by economic gain, particularly in times of economic hardship, as opposed to arranging a marriage with the daughter's overall interests in mind. When the bride's price has to be returned should the marriage fail, the bride's family may often take strong steps to prevent divorce even if the woman is suffering; since women often depend for their survival on husbands or the men in their family, they will often have no other choice but to accept their fate.

OLDER WOMEN, POWER AND FGM

FGM is said to be guarded by women, particularly the older women in the family and in the community. How do older women end up as custodians of FGM? The young bride normally moves from her family household to her husband's polygamous and extended family. Her role, along with other co-wives, is to procreate, to work on the land and to service the extended family. A young bride living within an extended family unit will have little control over her life.

Generally, restrictions are placed on females before puberty and during the childbearing years. After the menopause patriarchal society has no need to control women's reproduction or sexuality

as they can no longer bear children. Older women gain much status and power within the family and have an interest in preserving the lineage in order to preserve the stability of the family.[7]

> '*As in many other societies the older women achieve a status
> more closely resembling that of men. They have influence and
> authority over the daughters still living at home. Mothers are
> greatly respected by their sons and sons have closer emotional ties
> to their mothers than their stern patriarchal fathers. Grandmoth-
> ers are respected as fathers, and great emphasis and pride is
> attached to the position of grandparent. It is at that stage of life
> when they would seem to approach full membership in their hus-
> band's and son's patrilineage, certainly they display an increas-
> ingly keen interest in its welfare and continuity. It is not
> surprising therefore, to find that they are most often the initiators
> of infibulation ceremonies for their grand-daughters and that
> they must be considered the chief perpetrators of the practice.*' [8]

Older women perpetuate the family model unto the next generation. This is not specific to African culture, neither is it surprising as women are generally viewed as torch-bearers of
traditions. It is women the world over who socialize children,
both male and female, into specific gender roles and therefore
can be said to collude in their own oppression.

It is not surprising that women, having been denied wider
societal power, will hang on to the little power they do have and
exercise it in the area over which they have most control, i.e. the
family. It is often not easy to acknowledge that part of the reason
why it is women themselves who perpetrate the practice with
such zeal lies within their own suffering. To acknowledge this is
not to apportion blame, but understanding of the psychosocial
processes gives a better understanding and a framework for
working with women.

EXCISORS AND FGM

Part of the reason for the continuation of the practice of FGM
lies in the fact that it is an irreplaceable source of revenue for
excisors. The current economic aspect of FGM and excisors is a

modern development resulting from the introduction of cash into traditional subsistence economies. The role of excisors varies within the different ethnic groups who practise FGM. In some places, such as Somalia, they are not respected, while in West Africa they wield a lot of power and have considerable status within traditional power structures. Most excisors are also traditional midwives. Some of these have extended roles as consultants in mother and child care and as counsellors for women, working through the ideological and religious belief system of the people. They are feared and at the same time respected by women and the community at large. It is not surprising that any attack on these women is perceived by many people as an attack on the respected older women of the community.

Paradoxically, excisors are the gatekeepers of traditional power bases for women, called 'secret societies' in West Africa. It can be difficult to understand how a power base for women could incorporate a mutilating practice, but it might be easier to view this as a space for women within a wider male dominated society. Some people have interpreted this as possibly a remnant of matriarchy. The evidence given is that when age sets are initiated together, bonding and sisterhood develop which last a lifetime. Because of the aggressive gender training which goes on within the secret societies others have come to view them as part and parcel of the traditional power base and, in common with older women, excisors also become custodians of male power.

FUNCTIONAL ASPECTS OF FGM

The practice of FGM is often surrounded by various ceremonies, celebrations and coming-of-age rituals. In communities where it is performed on age sets of girls, specific periods of the year, such as after the harvest, are designated for FGM. Thus it has become a focus for communities coming together to celebrate and to reinforce their identity, giving a compulsive element to the practice of FGM. To avoid creating a social vacuum in these communities, campaigns for its eradication will have to seek an alternative focus for celebration in the communities.

Men and FGM

The practice of FGM remains in the female sphere: women are largely the excisors and the direct perpetuators of the practice. However, it is also clear that they have ended up performing FGM as a result of their powerlessness in traditional male dominated societies. Women practise FGM to please men. If we are to make any headway in the campaign to stop genital mutilation of girls, we will need to address male attitudes and the question is: What are male attitudes towards FGM?

Many men point out that males undergo circumcision and similar rites of passage too and, as such, FGM is not a mechanism used by men to oppress women. There are similarities and dissimilarities between FGM and male circumcision and also between the rites of passage for boys and girls. Certainly the two procedures are related. Both are widely practised without medical necessity and in both cases children go through a traumatic experience. Both are performed on children without their consent. But there the parallel ends. The clitoris is biologically equivalent to the penis. Clitoridectomy, which is the most common form of FGM, is analogous to penisectomy rather than to circumcision. Male circumcision involves cutting the tip of the protective hood of skin that covers the penis but does not damage the penis, the organ for sexual pleasure. Clitoridectomy damages or destroys the organ for sexual pleasure in the female. The content of male rites of passage is geared towards training young boys to develop skills associated with power and control, not to reinforce their submissiveness and to make them feel they are second-class citizens as is done in the female initiation. Male circumcision is not perceived by African communities as a practice aimed at reducing the sexuality of men; on the contrary it is perceived as enhancing their virility.

There are conflicting accounts of the African male attitude towards FGM. Many dismiss it as women's business but at the same time refuse to marry excised or infibulated women. Many would not take a public stand on FGM although in private they may profess to be against the practice. Fathers have equally ambiguous positions.

Most men in rural and poor communities practising FGM have not been given the opportunity to give their opinion on female genital mutilation. Below are a number of understandable responses by men from a diversity of cultures practising FGM which the author has come across:

'We do not want our women to be prostitutes.'

'We do not want any women's liberation here. This is our culture. The Western culture is degenerate. You have been indoctrinated by feminism which is alien to our culture. The feminists are a group of masturbators obsessed with orgasm.'[9]

'Oh, the African intellectual hysteria! People cannot even get a roof over their heads and they are talking about this. There are more important problems to deal with. '

'My wife, mother and grandmother have had it done, and they are not complaining. When these foreigners talk about female circumcision, I asked them what do they know ? I tell them to go and ask my grandmother.'

'You want our women to be lesbians?'

On the other hand, some men risk the breakup of their marriage and families to protect their daughters, sisters or nieces from genital mutilation. Some are genuinely appalled when the facts of the practice are made known to them and some are active in the campaign against FGM in their communities. Male doctors in the Sudan and in Egypt have also been active in the anti-FGM campaign since the 1940s and have done valuable research on FGM which has given other campaigners a basis for action. Some men have complained that FGM has distorted the sexual relationship between themselves and their partners.[10]

I think the important issue here is that men are also victims of patriarchy; one cannot make any generalizations. Since FGM persists in male-dominated societies it is crucial to direct the campaign also at men.

Socialization of the female child

> *'The chief contribution of the family in patriarchy is the social-*
> *ization of the young into patriarchal ideology's prescribed atti-*
> *tudes towards the categories of role, temperament, and status.'* [11]

The discrimination against women in society starts in childhood. In patrilineal societies, male preference is very strong and at birth girls will not be as welcomed to the family as boys. It is not uncommon for women to be divorced if they continue to produce girls. They start working at a very young age, from six onwards, while their brothers are still playing. In the household, they take care of younger children and do simple household chores.

Girls are socialized to be self-effacing, obedient, humble, respectful and hard working. It is not uncommon for mothers to withdraw their daughters from school when their workload becomes unbearable so that they can help in the home, in the fields and with trading. Girls learn at an early age that their role is to service the needs of the family. Girls are married off very young, even as young as nine years old. Sometimes they are betrothed at birth. Before they have the chance to be biologically developed they have had babies.

Girls' physical growth is grossly affected not only by a lack of nourishing food but by the maldistribution of food in the home. The result is often the formation of narrow pelvises which later cause problems during childbirth. In addition, to preserve virginity, chastity and 'purity' for marriage, limits and prohibitions are placed on the girl's freedom of movement and association.

One African President who made a statement showing the linkage between the position of women in society and FGM was the late head of state of Burkina Faso, Thomas Sankara. The following is an extract from a statement he made on FGM:

> *'When a man takes his daughters for excision, independently of*
> *any cultural and mystical values he wishes and tries to impart to*
> *his act, there is a clear difference in the care he shows for his*
> *small sons who go to be circumcized and the care, or rather the*
> *contempt, disdain and disregard he shows for his daughters in*

*handing them over to undergo a form of butchery. It also shows
an attempt to confer an inferior status on women by branding
them with this mark which diminishes them and is a constant
reminder to them that they are only women, inferior to men, that
they do not even have any rights over their own bodies or fulfilment either bodily or personal. They have limits imposed on them
by men.'*

*'As we can view male circumcision as being a measure of
hygiene, in the same way we can only see excision as a measure
of inferiorization.'* [12]

RIGHTS OF WOMEN

Female genital mutilation is thus an extreme example of the general subjugation of women, sufficiently extreme and horrifying to
make women and men question the basis of what is done to
women, what women have accepted and why, in the name of
society and tradition.

The burning of Indian widows and the binding of the feet of
Chinese female children are other striking examples, sharp
enough and strange enough to throw a spotlight on other less
obvious ways in which women the world over submit to oppression. All these practices are, or were, preserved under centuries
upon centuries of tradition: foot binding was only finally stopped
by massive social and political revolution which swept away
many other traditions as well.

To be successful, campaigns against female genital mutilation
should not only eliminate but replace the custom. Furthermore,
such success may only come about through long-term changes in
attitudes and ideologies by both men and women.

A major international expression of the goal of equal rights for
women was made in December 1979, when the United Nations
(UN) General Assembly adopted the Convention on the Elimination of All Forms of Discrimination Against Women. This came
into force in September 1981. This comprehensive convention
calls for equal rights for women, regardless of their marital status,
in all fields – political, economic, social, cultural and civil. Article

5(a) obliges signatory states to take:

'All appropriate measures to modify the social and cultural patterns of conduct of men and women, with a view to achieving the elimination of prejudices and customary and all other practices which are based on the idea of the inferiority or superiority of either of the sexes or on stereotyped roles for men and women.'

The Vienna Declaration which emerged from the UN World Human Rights Conference in 1993 stressed (in part 11, paragraph 9) that:

'The human rights of women and of a girl-child are an inalienable, integral and indivisible part of universal human rights.'

To succeed in abolishing the practice of FGM will demand fundamental attitudinal shifts in the way that society perceives the human rights of women.

RIGHTS OF CHILDREN

FGM violates the human rights of children when performed on infants and on young children. The fundamental issue at stake here is that of informed consent. An adult is quite free to submit her or himself to a ritual or a tradition, but a child, having no formed judgement, does not consent but simply undergoes the operation (which in this case is irrevocable) while she is totally vulnerable.

The descriptions available of the reactions of the children – panic and shock from extreme pain, biting through the tongue, convulsions, it taking six adults to hold down an eight-year old girl sometimes leading to fractures of the clavicle, femur or humerus, and death – indicate a practice comparable to torture.

Many governments violate Article 5 of the Universal Declaration of Human Rights (which provides that no one shall be subjected to torture, or cruel, inhuman or degrading treatment). These violations are discussed and sometimes condemned by various UN commissions. FGM, however, is a question of torture inflicted not on adults but on girl children, and the reasons given are not concerned with either political conviction or military necessity but are solely in the name of tradition.

Other treaties which are violated are the African Charter on the Rights and Welfare of the Child, where Article 21 stresses that 'Appropriate measures can be taken in order to eradicate traditional practices and customs which are prejudicial to the child.'

Another relevant international treaty is the Convention on the Rights of the Child. Article 2 protects the child's rights to gender equality; Article 19.1 protects the child from all forms of mental and physical violence and maltreatment; Article 24.1 states the right of the child to the highest attainable standard of health; Article 37(a) states that children should be free from torture or cruel, inhuman degrading treatment; and Article 24.3 of the Convention explicitly requires states to take all effective and appropriate measures to abolish traditional practices prejudicial to the health of children.

Those treaties which have been ratified by UN member states should not remain merely pieces of paper, but their provisions should be translated into specific mechanisms for the protection of girl children.

THE RIGHT TO GOOD HEALTH

No reputable medical practitioner would agree that mutilation is good for the physical or mental health of females while a growing number offer research and case histories indicating its grave permanent damage to health, underlining the risks of death. Removing the female organ of sexual pleasure leads to sexual dysfunction which has a deleterious effect on the mental health of the person. Health rights are guaranteed by the Universal Declaration of Human Rights (Article 25), the International Covenants on Economic, Social and Cultural Rights (Article 12), the Convention on the Rights of the Child (Article 2.4) and the African Charter on Human and People's Rights (Article 16). Finally, equal rights to health care are guaranteed by the Convention on the Elimination of All Forms of Discrimination Against Women (Article 12).

Medical facts, carefully explained, may be one way to discourage the practice, since these facts are almost the opposite of what is believed, and can be demonstrated and proved.

Those UN agencies and government departments specifically entrusted with the health needs of women and children must realize that it is their responsibility to support positive and specific preventative programmes aimed at female genital mutilation, for while the practice continues women's health and quality of life will inevitably suffer. However, this approach, if presented out of context, ignores the force of societal pressures which drive women to perform these operations, regardless of risk,in order to guarantee marriage for their daughters, and to conform to severe codes of female behaviour laid down by male-dominated societies.

THE RIGHT TO DEVELOPMENT

The practice of FGM must be seen in the context of underdevelopment[13] and the realities of life for the most vulnerable and exploited sectors – women and children. International political and economic forces have frequently prevented development to a level which meets the basic needs of rural populations. With no access to education or resources, and with no effective power base, the rural and urban poor cling to traditions as a survival mechanism in times of socio-economic change.

In societies where marriage for a woman is her only means of survival, and where some form of excision is a prerequisite for marriage, persuading her to relinquish the practice for herself or for her children is an extraordinarily difficult task. Female (and some male) African analysts of development strategies are today constantly urging that the generally deteriorating conditions in which poor women live be made a major focus for change,[14] for unless development changes their lives for the better, traditional practices are unlikely to be relinquished.

4

INTERNATIONAL INITIATIVES AND ACTION

'In fact, the solution of the problem of women will be collective and international. Change in their status will be at this price or not at all.'

Awa Thiam, Senegal[1]

Is female genital mutilation an international issue or does it only concern the countries directly affected? FGM now exists in many countries of the world, partly because ethnic groups and religions straddle international boundaries, but also because millions of people, especially in Africa, have been forced to flee their countries as refugees. It is rightly considered, therefore, as an international issue. It is also a human rights issue which has an impact on the health of millions of girl children and adult women. Since children particularly do not have a voice of their own, that alone should make FGM a major international human rights issue.

The history of the campaign for FGM's abolition indicates that there have been varying levels of activity undertaken by individuals, non-government organizations and the UN on FGM over a long period of time. All have led progressively to the breaking down of the walls of silence surrounding FGM. An overview of how this happened, the difficulties and the major contributions to bringing about change, is presented in this chapter.

EARLY EFFORTS

Efforts to combat FGM have a long history both in and outside Africa. In the past, individual health professionals have tried to raise community awareness of the health dangers associated with the practice. These people were isolated and because their efforts were scattered and were not recorded, it was difficult to assess the degree of impact they had on their communities. It is known, however, that the practice of female genital mutilation was opposed by the early Christian missionaries in Africa from the late seventeenth century onwards and that, in the 1940s, the British colonial administration, jointly with Sudanese professionals and religious bodies, made attempts to ban FGM in Sudan. However, these efforts were met with resistance as people saw them as part of an attempt to destroy their culture. As the colonial administration and the missionaries did not want to alienate their subjects or converts over this issue, they backed off from further intervention.

UN involvement in the issue of FGM

The middle years of the twentieth century were a period of change for many countries, particularly in Africa, which were shaking off their colonial administrators and beginning to run themselves independently. Initially, most of the new governments concentrated on overtly political and economic issues, rather than the cultural sphere, and so did little to combat the practice of FGM. Meanwhile, there was a feeling after the Second World War that the concept of human rights ought to be available to all people and nations and it was in this spirit that, in 1958, the Economic and Social Council (ECOSOC) of the United Nations invited the World Health Organization (WHO) to: 'undertake a study of the persistence of customs which subject girls to ritual operations, and of the measures adopted or planned for putting a stop to such practices,'[2] and to communicate the results of that study to the Commission on the Status of Women before the end of 1960. The twelfth WHO Assembly in 1959 rejected this request on the grounds that: 'the ritual operations in question are based on social and cultural backgrounds, the study of which is outside the competence of the World Health Organization'.[3]

WHO was again asked to undertake a study on the subject by the African participants in a UN seminar in Addis Ababa, 'On the Participation of Women in Public Life', and this request was repeated by ECOSOC (Resolution 821 11 (XXXII) adopted 19 July 1961).

Both requests were again rejected and, as a result, there were no further substantive initiatives at the UN level for nearly twenty years.

The UN Decade for women

The international interest in FGM resurfaced during the United Nations Decade for Women (1975-85). The decade brought into sharp focus the status of women in society, in particular the depressed status of women in the developing countries. FGM was raised at the mid-decade UN conference held in Copenhagen in July 1980, to review past progress, concentrating on the sub-themes: health, education and employment. In the 'Review and Evaluation of Progress Achieved in the Implementation of the (1975) World Plan of Action: Health' (document A/CONF. 94/9), the subject of female genital mutilation was mentioned once under the sub-heading 'Cultural practices affecting women's health':

'Paragraph 45. Female circumcision and infibulation can lead to complications during pregnancy. The Second Regional Conference on the Integration of Women in Development, held at Lusaka from 3rd to 7th December 1979, condemned sexual mutilation practices, but was also critical of uninformed international campaigns against these practices, and called upon Governments and women's organizations to seek solutions to the problem.'

In the main policy document of the conference, the 'Programme of Action for the Second Half of the United Nations Decade for Women: Equality, Development and Peace', the subject was not referred to at all by name. Under the section: 'Objectives and priority areas for action taken in connection with the sub-theme of the World Conference, Employment, Health and Education', paragraph 129 refers to the promotion of: 'extensive health education programmes, including special efforts to encourage positive traditional practices, especially breast-feeding, and to combat negative practices detrimental to women's health.'

No African country took up the issue of female genital mutilation in the official conference. Due to pressure from the Swedish public, the Swedish delegation mentioned the subject, indicating that the Swedish authorities were prepared to support activities undertaken by the countries concerned but would take no action of their own in this respect.

It was the Copenhagen Non-Governmental Organizations Forum, a parallel gathering to the official conference, which brought the issue to international attention. This more informal group brought together 8,000 women from 120 countries to discuss and plan action on issues of importance to women through workshops and round-table discussions on specific subjects, panel debates on more general themes, films, slide-shows, lectures and press conferences.

It became evident from the beginning the extent to which 'female circumcision', as it was largely referred to, was a sensitive subject. The media coverage tended to be 'sensation-prone', focusing upon the process and symptoms of the practice rather than the reasons behind it. Some participants felt that the effect was detrimental, as it increased hostility from decision-makers in the mainly African countries concerned. On the other hand, it was frequently stressed that some years ago it would have been impossible in most countries even to mention the subject in public.

The three pre-planned workshops on the topic expanded to at least seven more. Several groups of participants could be distinguished: those from eastern Africa; those from West Africa; those from Europe and the USA; African immigrants in Europe; Africans studying in Europe. Each had a different point of view.

The eastern African delegates came from countries where the practices were more severe and campaigns against them more advanced. For example, in the Sudan, where campaigns against mutilation were well advanced, and the College of Nursing and

Midwifery educated against the practice, an educational booklet in Arabic had been developed, and concrete programmes had been started in rural areas with financial assistance from an organization in Sweden. Kenya had also started a similar project, financed from the same source. Edna Adan Ismail from Somalia, where over 90% of female children were infibulated, described the ways in which the support of her government had been obtained for research and preventative education programmes.

On the other hand, delegates from West African countries were at first shocked and unable to understand the interest shown. They stressed that abolition of these practices was not a priority for them, sufficient food and clean water having a far greater importance. Expressions of concern were interpreted as outside interference from colonial and neo-colonial states. Representatives from Burkina Faso declared themselves most shocked that the subject was discussed in a session with a French woman in the chair who had no experience of living in an African country. They severely reproached a writer from the USA and did in fact leave a meeting in protest.

The forum discussions probably made some Westerners who initially had strong views on immediate abolition of this 'barbaric custom' think again. They became convinced that the only efficient way to support African women working against the practice was by financing and supporting specific projects and educational activities planned and implemented by and with those in the countries concerned, and on their terms. As a result of the interaction and discussions at the forum, many women (both African and Western) came to realize that the high degree of emotion that they felt on this subject was, to some extent, a projection of their feelings of degradation and sexual abuse, which erupted when faced with such tangible examples of maltreatment of female genital organs.

The UN Commission on Human Rights

Since the subject of FGM was reintroduced onto the agenda of the UN Commission on Human Rights in 1981, several resolutions have been adopted, and one regional seminar has been organized in Ougadougou, Burkina Faso, from 29 April to 3 May 1991, to assess the human rights aspects of FGM and certain traditional practices affecting women and children. The seminar provided the opportunity for the exchange of information and experience between national officials in the regions in question, the specialized agencies concerned, some United Nations organs and non-governmental organizations.

From the detailed discussions which took place, it was observed that, despite the seriousness of the problems and the numerous resolutions and recommendations adopted at international, regional and national levels, the question of FGM and other harmful traditional practices had not received the attention they deserved from the states concerned. In the view of the participants in the seminars, such practices persist because of the lack of political will on the part of many states, and the failure to inform and educate the population. Leaders of public opinion, political parties, religious leaders, trade unions, legislators, educators, medical practitioners and the mass media have not been sufficiently aware of the negative impact of these harmful traditional practices on an important sector of society.[4]

The United Nations Commission on Human Rights (UNCHR) proposed the following plan with a view to the introduction of concrete and positive changes to redress the situation at both national and international levels.

THE UNCHR PLAN OF ACTION FOR
ELIMINATION OF HARMFUL PRACTICES
AFFECTING THE HEALTH OF WOMEN AND CHILDREN
First the UNCHR recommended national action and the key features of its recommendations are as follows:-
1 A clear expression of political will and an undertaking to put an end to traditional practices negatively affecting the health of women and girl children, particularly female genital mutilation, is required on the part of governments concerned.
2 International instruments, including those relating to the protection of women and children, should be ratified and effectively implemented.

3   Legislation prohibiting practices harmful to the health of women and children, particularly female genital mutilation, should be drafted.
4   Governmental bodies should be created to implement the official adopted policy.

It also recommended action, the key features of which are:
1   The Commission on the Status of Women should give more attention to harmful traditional practices.
2   Intergovernmental organizations and specialized agencies and bodies of the UN system should integrate into their activities the issue of confronting harmful traditional practices.
3   All the organs of the United Nations working for the protection of children and for the promotion of human rights in particular, that is the International Convention of the Elimination of All Forms of Discrimination Against Women; the Convention on the Rights of the Child; and the Covenants on Human Rights and the Convention Against Torture should include the question of harmful traditional practices which jeopardize the health of women and of girls and discriminate against them.

Finally, the participation of non-governmental organizations is crucial for the elimination of harmful traditional practices and the Commission recommended that:
1   National and international non-governmental organizations concerned with protecting the health of women and children should include in their programmes activities relating to traditional practices affecting the health of women and girl children.
2   Non-governmental organizations should continue to reinforce their activities in favour of protecting the human rights of women and girl children.

At the United Nations First World Conference on Human Rights, held in Vienna in 1993, gender-based violence was recognized as a human rights issue. This included FGM. The Vienna Declaration and Programme of Action devotes several pages to the 'equal status and human rights of women as a priority for governments' and it sounded an historic call for the elimination of 'violence against women in public and private life' as a human rights obligation.[5] In March 1994, the UNCHR appointed Ms Radhika Coomaraswamy from Sri Lanka as the Commission on Human Rights' Special Rapporteur on violence against women. She will be reporting to the Commission on an annual basis. Female genital mutilation and other practices such as domestic violence, infanticide and incest are classified under the category of violence in the family, in the Vienna Declaration and Programme of Action.[6]

UN specialized agencies

RESPONSE TO FGM
The UN Specialized Agencies directly involved in women's health and children's welfare were very slow to respond to FGM. The WHO began to be active from 1976 when its Regional Office for the Eastern Mediterranean undertook a review of the medical literature on FGM and followed this up with a seminar in 1979, but only after repeated requests by UN ECOSOC and by concerned individuals.

One would also have expected UNICEF to be at the forefront of the campaign for the abolition of FGM, a practice which affects millions of girls in Africa, since UNICEF has children's programmes all over Africa. However, it too only became active on the subject in March 1980.

UNESCO maintains almost total silence on FGM. It has not been discussed at any of the many conferences and debates nor included in research studies on cultural patterns in Africa, social change, education or human rights, not even during the International Year of the Child in 1979. No UNESCO personnel in the field collect information, stimulate research or assist with education campaigns.

The UN Specialized Agencies are intergovernmental and take their mandates for their work from the UN's member states. Any preventative work on FGM done by these Agencies has to be placed within the interest of the work they do generally with women and girls. For the most part, women's sexual, gynaecological and mental health needs were not appreciated in the past nor given the priority which they deserved by member states. The focus of women's health programmes was on childbearing and fertility control. The UN Specialized Agencies could not be pro-active on FGM without a mandate from member states.

Second, FGM is a girl's and women's health and human rights issue. Female human rights, e.g., in the area of gender-based violence against women, are just beginning to be recognized internationally. This has come about as a result of the work of women themselves in the last fifteen years, triggered off by the UN Decade for Women. Women have broadened the understanding of human rights to emphasize women's human rights and have made linkages between health and human rights. They have also campaigned to place their needs on various agendas including those of the UN Specialized Agencies.

Last, and most important, FGM was unlike other straightforward issues such as immunization or the control of malaria and diarrhoea, diseases with which the UN Specialized Agencies were familiar. It is not a disease, rather (as we have seen) it is part of the social control of girls and women in many developing countries – but with profound health consequences – and as such it is a very 'sensitive' and difficult area in which to work. Women who have themselves undergone FGM are its strongest defenders. Until there was a stirring against FGM among women in the countries directly concerned, these Agencies felt they could not be active in the campaign to abolish the practice.

Rather than take a lead in the campaign and risk a backlash from women and governments in the countries directly concerned, the UN Specialized Agencies diplomatically tried to generate interest in the subject of FGM through conferences, meetings and workshops to promote recommendations and statements aimed primarily at those countries.[7,8] They also collaborated with international NGOs which sought a way round the problem by supporting the development of indigenous African groups to undertake advocacy work with governments and to facilitate work on FGM in African countries.

Contributions made by UN Specialized Agencies towards the Eradication of FGM

THE WORLD HEALTH ORGANIZATION

Seminar Recommendations
The first opportunity for discussion provided by the WHO was the seminar on 'Traditional Practices Affecting the Health of Women and Children', organized by WHO Regional Office for the Eastern Mediterranean in Khartoum, in February 1979. Representatives from ten countries participated: Djibouti, Oman, Egypt, Somalia, South Yemen, Ethiopia, Kenya, Nigeria, Burkina Faso and, of course, Sudan.

The following actions were recommended by the seminar and addressed primarily to the governments concerned:
1 Adoption of clear national policies for the abolition of female circumcision.
2 Establishment of national commissions to co-ordinate and follow up the activities of the bodies involved including, where appropriate, the enactment of legislation prohibiting female circumcision.
3 Intensification of general education of the public, including health education at all levels, with special emphasis on the dangers and undesirability of female circumcision.
4 Intensification of education programmes for traditional birth attendants, midwives, healers and other practitioners of traditional medicine, to demonstrate the harmful effects of female circumcision, with a view to enlisting their support, along with general efforts to abolish this practice.

These recommendations were implemented only to a limited extent by governments directly concerned. However this seminar was a major breakthrough in the campaign. WHO gave its name and credibility to NGOs and campaigners working directly in the field through this seminar. For the first time, they could refer to the WHO recommendations and their work could be accepted.

Health professionals: policy on medicalization of FGM
In 1982 the WHO issued a statement against the medicalization of FGM,[9] which continues to be a useful advocacy tool for campaigners in the field.

The WHO supports the development of the Inter-African Committee on Traditional Practices Affecting the Health of Mothers and Children with its national chapters in all countries.

Research
The WHO co-sponsored a major country-wide study, 'An epidemiological Study of Female Circumcision in the Sudan', 1980/81.[10]

In May 1994, the World Health Assembly, the WHO Executive Board, adopted a resolution on traditional practices harmful to the health of women and children. This development was possible as the motion was proposed with the backing of some African member states. It is now possible for the WHO to work directly on this issue and already the Division of Family Health at its headquarters in Geneva has started work on FGM.

UNICEF
In March 1980 a meeting of WHO and UNICEF came up with a joint 'plan of action' endorsing a 'through primary health care' approach, and laying down as an essential principle that all activity should be undertaken through citizens of the countries involved.

The plan recommended:
1 Strong advocacy efforts directed towards WHO/UNICEF staff, national policy and decision-makers, all health and health-related personnel, and the general public.
2 The identification and support of organizations with national structures and credibility in the field.
3 Fostering action-orientated research on epidemiology, and socio-cultural studies encompassing behaviour, values and attitudes.
4 The dissemination of the results of successful action and research in practising countries.
UNICEF stressed that the implementation of these recommenda-

tions was to be the responsibility of each individual UNICEF country or area representative and the appropriate government authorities.

Like the WHO, UNICEF supported the setting up of the Inter-African Committee (IAC) on Harmful Traditional Practices in 1984. At country level UNICEF has given funding support to the IAC in its mobilization and awareness creating activities in the anti-FGM campaign.

UNFPA
UNFPA is funding FGM related activities including support for the formation of the IAC, and has provided funding for its development and activities in the field.

The International Conference on Population and Development (ICPD) held in Cairo in September 1994 had the following sentence in its final declaration:

> *'Governments are urged to prohibit female genital mutilation wherever it exists and to give vigorous support to non-governmental and community organizations, and religious institutions to eliminate such practices.'*[11]

RESPONSE OF INTERNATIONAL NON-GOVERNMENTAL ORGANIZATIONS

Many international NGOs, for example Amnesty International, had found it difficult in the past to work on FGM as a women's human rights issue. This is because it does not fit into a neat traditional category of torture, e.g. dictatorial governments torturing political prisoners. FGM is gender-based violence which happens in the home, is condoned by the family and the community at large and over a period of time has been accepted as culture. As a human rights issue it falls into the category of citizen upon citizen abuse. It is not governments who are forcing girls to be mutilated. Governments become implicated when they do not take action to protect girls from this form of torture. So how can the international agencies respond to FGM?

FGM is one of those women's human rights issues which

requires a strategic approach to prevention. Some international NGO's have started the process. Examples of their activities are presented below.

The NGO Working Group on Traditional Practices Affecting The Health of Women and Children

The NGO Working Group was formed in Geneva in 1977 by members of non-governmental organizations having consultative status with the Economic and Social Council of the United Nations. Membership comprised of 26 international NGOs, which formed part of the Special Committee on the Status of Women. The NGO Working Group concerned itself exclusively with excision and its grave consequence for women's heath, and reflected on the most effective way of combating these practices. It became clear to them that they should interest themselves in the training of medical and social workers who were in contact with rural populations, and also in informing these populations. In order that these two initiatives – training and information – should have a chance of success, it was necessary to obtain the agreement and co-operation both of official bodies and of women directly concerned.

Mrs Isabelle Tevoedjre from Benin, the former co-ordinator of the NGO Working Group, was the wife of a senior African UN official based in Geneva; she and the late Mrs Margareta Linnander, the UN representative of the London based Anti-Slavery Society (now Anti-Slavery International), made an excellent pair in undertaking diplomatic activities on FGM in Africa. With financial assistance from Radda Barnen (Swedish Save The Children) and later from the late Dr Gordon Wallace of the US-based Population Crises Committee (now Population Action International), they travelled extensively and met with presidents, senior politicians and members of women's organizations. Their discussions led them to understand that by means of modest development projects at village level, it would be possible gradually to bring to the attention of women the dangers of excision.

The first projects started in Kenya and in the Sudan. Under cover of activities orientated towards specific areas of women's interest, talks on health education were organized two or three times a month. These covered family planning, nutrition, care of pregnant women and children, and, above all, excision and its grave consequences. These health education talks were carried out by trained African doctors, midwives, nurses and birth attendants.[12]

Mrs Berhane Ras-Work from Ethiopia, also the wife of an Ethiopian UN official in Geneva, took over the role of co-ordinator of the NGO Working Group in 1983 from Isabelle Tevoedjre who was returning to her home country, and she and the late Mrs Margareta Linnander continued the diplomatic and advocacy work on FGM in Africa. They lobbied politicians, government officials and women's organizations on the issue of harmful traditional practices. The groundwork covered by the two diplomats was impressive.

The NGO Working Group had done considerable advocacy work on FGM in the UN Commission on Human Rights and the Sub-Commission of Human Rights on female genital mutilation. The Group followed up the Minority Rights Group and the author's intervention on FGM at the Human Rights Commission in 1981 and 1982, by lobbying for the appointment of a Special Rapporteur, and for the Commission to set up a UN Working Group on Traditional Practices. The NGO Working Group also worked on the Convention on the Rights of the Child. The NGO Working Group drafted Article 24(3) on harmful traditional practices[13] in the UN Convention of the Rights of the Child, basing it on Article 21 of the African Charter on the Rights and Welfare of the Child which states that:

'*appropriate measures be taken in order to eradicate traditional practices and customs which are prejudicial to the child*',

and lobbied for its inclusion in the Convention. It also lobbied the UN Specialized Agencies – the WHO and UNICEF – on FGM.

In 1984 it made a major breakthrough by organizing a regional seminar on Traditional Practices Affecting the Health of Women and Children in Africa in collaboration with the Ministry of Public Health, Senegal, the WHO, UNICEF and UNFPA in Dakar, Senegal. This seminar resulted in the formation of the

Inter-African Committee (IAC) on Traditional Practices Affecting the Health of Women and Children. The NGO Working Group has continued with its support for the IAC.

The Inter-African Committee on Traditional Practices Affecting the Health of Women and Children

The IAC has the following aims:

1   To reduce the morbidity and mortality rates of women and children through the eradication of harmful traditional practices.
2   To promote traditional practices which are beneficial to the health of women and children, to play an advocacy role by promoting the importance of action against harmful traditional practices at international, regional and national levels.
3   To raise funds and to support local activities of national committees and other partners.

Under the leadership of Mrs Berhane Ras-work, the IAC has worked tirelessly to set up 24 national committees in the following countries: Benin, Burkina Faso, Cameroon, Chad, Djibouti, Egypt, Ethiopia, Gambia, Ghana, Guinea-Bissau, Ivory Coast, Kenya, Liberia, Mali, Niger, Nigeria, Senegal, Sierra Leone, Somalia, Sudan, Tanzania, Togo, Ugandia.

The main focus of the IAC activities is first, the training and information Campaign (TIC). The TIC training workshops are aimed at providing intensive health education with the help of visual aids. The subjects discussed are related to FGM, early childhood marriage, human reproduction, pregnancy, childbirth, breast-feeding adn hygiene as well as to nutritional taboos.

The programme consists of four sets of training workshops, to be conducted consecutively over five months. After each TIC programme is completed, 28 persons will have been trained to be able to conduct sensitization programmes on the harmful effects of FGM and other traditional practices, and a further 136 persons will have attended workshops and will spread information regarding these issues.

Second, the IAC promotes training of Traditional Birth Attendants (TBA) so that they can play an important role in the campaign against harmful traditional practices.

Third, the IAC produces educational materials, including anatomical models, flannelgraphs, simple viewers with a set of slides, multi-media training modules and materials which are targeted to reach four major groups: women in influential positions; students and youth groups; teachers; religious and community leaders and paramedical staff. The IAC has produced a video 'Beliefs and Misbeliefs', which explains the dangers of FGM and shows what the IAC does in Africa. Finally, the IAC produces a newsletter twice a year, in English and French.

The IAC collaborates with the WHO, UNICEF, UNFPA, UN Centre of Human Rights, the OAU and the Economic Commission for Africa. It now has consultative status with the UN ECOSOC and observer status with the OAU.[14]

Minority Rights Group

Minority Rights Group (MRG) is an international research and information unit registered in the UK as an educational charity.

In 1980, MRG published a report on FGM, entitled *Female Circumcision, Excision and Infibulation: the facts and proposals for Change*, containing contributions from a number of African women campaigners and edited by Scilla Elworthy (formerly McLean). It was published at a time when the existence of the practice was becoming known to an international audience, notably through conferences organized during the UN Decade for Women. Yet basic facts surrounding the practice were frequently presented in a distorted, sensationalist and somewhat racist way. By presenting information in a logical, coherent and unemotional manner, MRG hoped both to increase awareness on the subject of female genital mutilation and to stimulate support for women and men working towards its eradication. Rather than righteous indignation, what was urgently needed was understanding of the problem and practical support to change it. Furthermore, the issue needed to be placed on the programmes of the international agencies and on the human rights agenda.

The response to this report when it was first published in December 1980 was overwhelming. Not only did it receive sympathetic attention from the UK and international press, but hundreds of women and men sent contributions to support those who were fighting the practice. In the wake of this interest, the Women's Action Group Against Excision and Infibulation (WAGFEI) was formed, made up of African, Arab and British men and women. The author became its co-ordinator. WAGFEI set itself specific tasks which included carrying our fact-finding missions in Africa and directed funds to small projects in Egypt, Sudan, Somalia and Kenya.

The first TV documentary on the subject, produced by Louise Panton (*Forty Minutes*, BBC2), which outlined the health problems associated with FGM, was made with the assistance of WAGFEI. This was shown in the UK in 1983. Copies were distributed to campaigners in Africa and to international development agencies.

One of WAGFEI's tasks was to promote the voice of African women internationally and its efforts led to the publication of Dr Asma El Dareer's book *Women, Why Do You Weep? Circumcision and its Consequences*,[15] in 1982. WAGFEI facilitated the distribution of this book in Africa.

In August 1981, under the auspices of MRG, the author presented a detailed statement on genital mutilation, first to the UN Working Group on Slavery (Sub-Commission on the Protection of Minorities and the Prevention of Discrimination), and subsequently in February 1982 to the Commission on Human Rights. The statement urged the Commission to seek the appropriate channels to ensure that the governments concerned implemented the recommendations of the WHO 1979 Khartoum Seminar.

Following this intervention by the author, the Commission requested from governments information on the work which had been done to combat FGM. This in turn led to the formation of a Working Group on Traditional Practices and the appointment of a Special Rapporteur to further the work on FGM within the Human Rights Commission. MRG has continued to offer support and to collaborate with African women campaigning for the eradication of FGM by the wide distribution of the report on FGM.

Foundation for Women's Health Research and Development (FORWARD International)

FORWARD International (formerly known as FORWARD) developed from WAGFEI into an independent international organization in 1983, registered under the UK Charity Act. Its main aim is to promote good health amongst African women and children internationally.

FORWARD International worked with Lord Kennet, a member, of the House of Lords, to introduce the first FGM prohibition Bill in the UK Parliament, but it fell on technicalities. In 1985 new legislation was passed, however, prohibiting FGM in the UK. Through the support of Lord Kennet, FORWARD International was able to secure funding for education in the immigrant communities directly affected by the practice of FGM. In 1989 FORWARD International successfully lobbied the government to include FGM as a form of physical abuse within its child care law.

FORWARD International focused on developing multi-dimensional strategies in the eradication of FGM at the grassroots level. Models for prevention combined community action, emergency child protection measures, professional guidelines and training. This model, which was tested with the African immigrant communities, has been adopted by the UK Department of Health and local authorities. In July 1992, it organized the 'First Study Conference on Genital Mutilation of Girls in Europe', which brought genital mutilation of girls outside Africa into the open and onto the international agenda. The Conference, which was attended by representatives from the UK Department of Health, various UK local authorities, community group leaders and professionals from Europe, the US and Canada, came out with the London Declaration which set up a framework for the abolition of FGM in Western countries. This framework has been adopted in many countries in Europe and Canada. In the US, FORWARD International collaborates with Equality Now, the international women's rights organization to brief senior staff at Congress and the US Agency for International Development on its national and international policy on FGM. Recently it provided an advisory support for Congresswoman Pat Schroeder on her private member's Bill to prohibit FGM in the USA.

FORWARD International publishes and distributes training manuals for professionals and for community workers internationally. The information pack; *Child Protection and Female Genital Mutilation, FGM and a Counselling Guide for Professionals*, is widely used by professionals and policy-makers in different countries.

FORWARD International runs a small consultancy service on FGM for decision-makers, local and health authorities, professional bodies and agencies in Western countries. International agencies such as the WHO and the World Bank have used its services, as well as bodies such as the Royal College of Nursing and the Swedish Board of Health and Social Welfare.

FORWARD International promotes awareness of FGM and has acted as consultant on several TV documentaries and radio programmes which have been transmitted internationally. In the US it supported the production of the ABC Day One Show *Scarred for Life* in 1993, by advising them to shoot a film on FGM in the Gambia within the context of initiation rituals and provided further guidance and links with local groups in the Gambia, and has contributed to several articles in magazines and journals. This input has had a catalytic effect in generating interest and funding support for activities to prevent FGM in Africa.

FORWARD International acts as enabler for community organizations' grassroots projects which include helping women to integrate FGM prevention within their existing activities and it backs up such initiatives with training and education materials. It collaborates with African campaigning groups such as the Inter-Africa Committee on Traditional Practices. In Ghana it funded the first research on FGM in the Upper East Region of Ghana and lobbied for the Gambian Women's Bureau to obtain funding for a study of FGM in the Gambia.

SPECIFIC PROJECTS OF FORWARD INTERNATIONAL

The following are some of the current projects it is working on:

1   'African Men Against Female Genital Mutilation' Project. This has an international membership and was initiated jointly by FORWARD International and the African Resource and Information Centre based in Ottawa, Canada. They are galvanizing African men internationally to take a stand against FGM and to be active in the anti-FGM campaign. The project is developing a training conference in Africa.

2   Young People's Project, which offers a counselling service to young girls and women in the UK on issues pertaining to FGM.

3   FORWARD International's Supporters Project allows members from around the world who do not come from FGM-practising communities to support the anti-FGM campaign in a practical way. For example, in 1993 Michael Coulston ran the London Marathon to support sending free education materials to Africa. In another instance supporters have sponsored the wages of a Somali interpreter to be based at the first African Well-Woman Clinic, Northwick Park Hospital, which provides speedy and specialized care for excised/infibulated women.

FORWARD International collaborates with governmental, non-governmental and international agencies, including the UK Department of Health, WHO and UN Centre for Human Rights, and networks with community groups, health and social work professionals and women's organizations internationally. It publishes a periodic newsletter, *Forward Links*.

Other international forums

The subject of FGM has been raised in several international forums and many resolutions have been passed.

1   In June 1982 the International Council of Nurses adopted a resolution against genital mutilation. In 1993 it adopted a statement concerning human rights recommending 'the need for nursing actions to safeguard human rights... where abuse of patients is suspected'.

2   At the Fourth International Congress on Child Abuse and Neglect (Paris, 7-10 September 1982) three workshops on the topic were given.

3   The International Seminar of the Commission pour L'Abolition des Mutilations Sexuelles (CAMS), held in Dakar, Senegal, 27-9 December 1982, voted to establish a research and education centre in Senegal towards the abolition of these practices.

4   A workshop 'African Women Speak' in October 1984, was organized by the Babiker Bedri Scientific Association for Women's Studies, Sudan. This brought together African women to discuss strategies for campaigns against female genital mutilation in their own countries and to plan for a workshop on traditional practices for the UN End of Decade Conference on Women, Nairobi, July 1985.

5   At the Nairobi conference marking the end of United Nations Women's Decade in July 1985, separate workshops on female genital mutilation were organized in the NGO forum by the Inter-Africa Committee on Traditional Practices and by Commission pour L'Abolition des Mutilations Sexuelles (CAMS).

6   In June 1985, in Mogadishu, Somalia, an International Seminar on 'Female Circumcision: Strategies to Bring About Change' was organized jointly by the Somali Women's Democratic Organization and the Italian Association for Women in Development.

7   In December 1988 in Paris, CAMS-France organized an international conference on 'Violence and Sexual Mutilation Inflicted on Girls and Women'.

8   From April to May 1991, the United Nations Human Rights Commission organized its first Seminar on 'Harmful Traditional Practices', in Ouagadougou, Burkina Faso.

INDIVIDUAL INITIATIVES

Several individuals' initiatives have been instrumental in informing the public, in Africa and elsewhere, of the existence and the extent of FGM practice. Some are presented below.

1   The research work carried out since 1973 by an intrepid American, Fran Hosken, resulted in her article 'The Epidemi-

ology of Female Genital Mutilations', published in *Tropical Doctor* in July 1976. She has kept up a barrage of questions to international agencies and NGOs to provoke action and enquiry; the *Women's International Network News* supplies regular information on this and other issues of vital importance to women the world over. In 1993, the fourth edition of the *Hosken Report – Genital and Sexual Mutilation of Females*, a comprehensive 450-page document, was published. *The Childbirth Picture Book* by Fran Hosken, with additional material aimed at preventing excisions and infibulation, is available in English, French, Arabic and Somali. The latter has been distributed free to non-governmental groups working for the eradication of FGM.

2   Articles by individuals began to appear in African publications, the first of which came out in 1975 in *Famille et Développement*, published in Dakar. An article by Esther Ogunmodede in the December 1977 issue of the magazine *Drum* made a big impact and in August 1978 a long article entitled 'The silence over female circumcision in Kenya' appeared in the magazine *Viva*, both African magazines.

3   In 1975 the Sudan Family Planning Associations (SFPA) magazine *Happy Family*, published the papers written on female genital mutilation in the Sudan contributing to the SFPA Seminar 'The role of Sudanese women in development', held in March 1975 in Khartoum. The SFPA then published a small booklet including all these articles, as well as the recommendations of the seminar. This booklet was widely distributed within the country.

4   The Swiss-based Terre des Hommes movement, which aids children in distress, called a widely reported press conference just before the WHO Assembly in Geneva in May 1977. They published two well-documented and illustrated reports on the subject.

5   The publication in France in 1978 of a book by a young Senegalese woman, Awa Thiam, on the situation of women in Africa, *La Parole aux Negresses*.[16] Awa Thiam became the president of CAMS which was established in France in 1980 and now has its headquarters in Dakar, Senegal. CAMS was a rally-

ing point for women to mobilize against FGM and other patriarchal practices in the early 1980s. Linda Weil-Curiel, a member of CAMS in France, has pioneered legal prosecutions over FGM in France.

6 In March 1979, Robin Morgan and Gloria Steinem wrote an article in *Ms* magazine 'The international crime of genital mutilation', to introduce the subject to its wide female readership both in the US and in Europe.

7 In December 1979, the African Symposium on 'The World of Work and the Protection of the Child', organized by the International Institute for Labour Studies in Yaounde, Cameroon, strongly recommended the organization of campaigns and of teaching by all educational means, on the dangers of excision. The symposium also urged the International Institute of Social Sciences to constitute a data bank on excision, in order to evaluate prevailing attitudes and debate the best ways of moving towards its eradication.

8 In 1982, two books on FGM published in London; *Sisters in Affliction*, by Raqiya Haji Dualeh Abdalla from Somalia, and *Women, Why Do You Weep?* by Asma El Dareer from the Sudan, increased international interest in FGM.[17]

9 In 1987, another book *The Circumcision of Women: A strategy for Eradication*, by Olayinka Koso-Thomas from Sierra Leone, was published, further raising the profile of African women internationally.[18]

10 In 1992, Alice Walker, the African-American, Pulitzer award-winning author, wrote a novel based on FGM entitled *Possessing the Secret of Joy*,[19] which has helped to bring the subject of FGM to a wider international audience. She followed this with another book on the subject, *Warrior Marks*[20], published in 1993, and a documentary of the same name made in collaboration with the English film producer Pratibha Parmar. This documentary has been shown in major cities in the USA, as well as in the UK at the Birmingham Film Festival, in France, Canada, Senegal and the Gambia. Alice Walker's work has sparked much interest and debate on the subject, particularly in the USA which has started to address its national and international policy on FGM.

11 Since 1992 Mr A.M. Rosenthal, has had a regular column on FGM in *The New York Times* and the *International Herald Tribune*. Senator Edward Kennedy has also been in the forefront of international advocacy on FGM with UN Specialized Agencies and the US Missions in Africa.

Conclusion

FGM has been a very complex and sensitive human rights issue to bring into the open. Breaking the silence on the practice through the contributions of individuals, feminists, non-governmental groups and international organizations such as the United Nations has been very painful. It brings to mind the history of other human rights actions such as the anti-slavery movement and, recently, the anti-apartheid movements. These human rights movements were successful only through international solidarity. Uprooting FGM in traditional patriarchal societies will come about at the same cost. Action has to be taken at different levels to abolish FGM. Everybody has a contribution to make in one form or the other. The greatest achievement of all is to empower African women to lead the campaign themselves, and much credit goes to the international NGOs for emphasizing this need. The work has just begun and there is a lot to be done to bring about change at grassroots level. The success of the anti-FGM campaign will demand better networking and solidarity. Genital mutilation of girls is a human problem and all people of goodwill should work together to eradicate it.

5

AFRICA – CASE STUDIES

*'We can't afford being different. We found our mothers circum-
cised; we learned that our grandmothers and great-grandmothers
were circumcised, and we have to carry the tradition to our children and grandchildren. We can't think of anyone who is not circumcised. Once a man divorced his wife as soon as he discovered
that, out of negligence, one of her two leaves was not cut off. This
man told his wife: "What have I married? A man or a woman?"
News of the incident spread and the woman did not know where
to hide because of the scandal.'*

Marie Assaad[1]

Over the past decade non-governmental activities
aimed at the abolition of female genital mutilation
have increased tremendously. In nearly all the countries where the practice of FGM persists, there now
exist anti-FGM groups. The groundwork achieved by groups
working to eradicate FGM is amazing, but what have been the
results of their efforts? It is a deeply rooted practice which has
existed within communities for many centuries and because it
used to be taboo, it was difficult for the individual to challenge
this practice. One of the major gains of the current campaigns to
combat FGM is that, at least in Africa, the ice has been broken
on the subject. Many people are now openly discussing it. While
the practice is common in all social classes and backgrounds,
there is increasing opposition to it among many educated parents. This is a major step towards its abolition.

Despite these major gains, millions of girls continue to be victims of this cruel practice. To bring about meaningful change at grassroots level will require creativity, concerted effort, patience and commitment. The current effort can only be strengthened by pausing to take stock, to learn from past campaigns and from the unique strategies which are evolving in different parts of Africa to combat FGM. There can be no blueprint for action within Africa as the local conditions of the different communities practising FGM vary greatly, but some general lessons can be drawn from past efforts which might be useful in the planning of future programmes. This chapter highlights some of these lessons and provides some pointers for future campaigns. It also presents information on the initiatives taken within the different countries to combat FGM.

CASE STUDY: THE SUDAN

In Sudan, attempts have been made to combat female genital mutilation for the past 50 years; yet today more than 80 per cent of women in Northern Sudan continue to be infibulated. Lessons may be learned from the experience of the Sudan, since it is the first country in Africa to have a record of legislating against the practice. Furthermore there have been several educational campaigns to combat FGM and some major scientific studies, which throw light on the impact of past campaigns.

In the 1930s a medical student submitted an article to a local government newspaper, in which he wrote openly about the effects of female genital mutilation and stressed that it should be abolished.[2] Sudan was under British colonial administration at the time and the authorities withheld the article for fear that conservative Sudanese might conclude that it was inspired by the British Government.[3]

In 1943, a Medical Committee was set up by the then Governor-General to study the problem of female genital mutilation, resulting in a booklet in Arabic and English, supported by religious leaders, which stated that 'pharaonic circumcision' (infibulation) was cruel and harmful, and should be abolished. This was supported by a press and radio campaign.

None of this had any discernible effect, so in 1946 the government resorted to legislation. Parents hurried to have their children infibulated before the law came into effect, resulting in a higher level of medical complications and deaths. Under the law, midwives performing infibulation were subject to a fine and imprisonment for up to seven years. Such violent disturbances greeted the first arrests that the law was amended and few further prosecutions made.

From the 1950s to the 1970s general education for both sexes advanced significantly but no major anti-FGM campaigns were undertaken. A milder, legal form of female genital mutilation was taught in midwifery schools, on the premise that if it was done, it should be done in an aseptic manner and inflict the minimum damage.

From the 1970s onwards the campaign against all forms of female genital mutilation recommenced. In 1975 the Sudan Family Planning Association held a seminar on 'Female Genital Mutilation' and in 1977 the fifth Congress of the Gynaecologists Society of the Sudan declared that female genital mutilation in all its forms should be abolished. In 1978, the Faculty of Medicine, in co-operation with the Ministry of Health and the WHO, started a field research project. The results showed that more than 90 per cent of the female population studied had undergone female genital mutilation.[4] In spite of all efforts in the clinical field, FGM persisted for socio-cultural reasons, largely because it had a ritual importance, but also for economic reasons, because it was a source of income for the midwife. Men continued to demand it of their prospective wives, and women continued to have it done since men demanded it. Influential people in various places defied the tradition, and while there were clusters of women who had not undergone FGM, they were relatively few.

By 1979, the midwifery schools no longer taught any technique, and midwifery trainees were urged to discontinue the practice. The Higher Nursing College taught a course in social ethics in which FGM was discussed as a mutilation, and the student nurses were made aware of the psychological as well as the medical consequences of the operation. The Department of

Social Welfare, with the support of UNICEF, produced a booklet entitled: *Pharaonic Female Circumcision – For It, Against It*. In the same year Ahfad University College for Women, in co-operation with interested community leaders, organized a symposium in Khartoum on female genital mutilation under the title 'The Changing Status of Sudanese Women.' The symposium called for the abolition of all forms of female genital mutilation. To implement the recommendations emanating from the seminar, a voluntary organization, the Babiker Bedri Scientific Association for Women's Studies (BBSAWS), named after the founder of women's education in the Sudan, was formed. In the succeeding years BBSAWS stimulated public debate and discussions on FGM.

In 1984, the Minister for Internal Affairs decreed the creation of a National Committee for the Eradication of Female Genital Mutilation in the Sudan. UNICEF, medical doctors, psychiatrists, educationalists, religious leaders, social workers, women's representatives and members of voluntary associations were included on the committee. Among its many functions it was to mobilize all forces within Sudanese society to fight FGM, to recommend legislation and other measures the government should adopt, and to co-ordinate national efforts directed towards the eradication of female genital mutilation. A number of meetings were held but the committee was unable to fulfil its mandate and in 1988, a new Sudanese National Committee for the Eradication of Traditional Practices Affecting the Health of Women and Children was formed. It had NGO status and it developed a plan of action focused on training and information campaigns.

The 1989-90 Sudanese Demographic and Health Survey (SDHS) included a questionnaire on female genital mutilation. The results indicated that 89 per cent of women who have been married had undergone genital mutilation, predominantly infibulation.[5] This figure represented a slight drop from the 96 per cent reported in the 1977-8 Sudan Fertility Survey. The SDHS study showed practically no difference in FGM prevalence by age.[6] A large majority (78 per cent) of women in northern Sudan still favour the continuation of FGM, although most would prefer a less severe form.[7] The study noted that the practice persisted largely because of tradition, and because of fear of social criticism and ignorance of its consequences. Educational opportunities for women in general seemed to loosen the hold of tradition.

Lessons from the Sudan experience

The major gap in the Sudan effort seems to be lack of a planned and sustained education programme for the eradication of FGM from the 1940s onwards. The practice is a major public health and a social hazard but governmental involvement in its eradication, after a burst of activities in the forties, is minimal. Governmental policy of allowing less radical forms of FGM to be practised, but legislating against infibulation appeared not to have worked; the law was barely enforced and attempts to medicalize FGM also failed.

Developing an effective response to FGM

One of the major gaps in the African campaign is that governmental child care monitoring systems are not fully developed to cover all children through the primary health care system or through schools. It is difficult, therefore, to work effectively and to respond quickly to protect children from traditional forms of abuse such as early and forced child marriages or female genital mutilation. Mass education and counselling against the practice should be the major thrust of the campaign for the abolition of FGM, but direct government involvement will also be necessary, including legal sanctions. Child protection law can be used in a preventative way, and this is an area which should be explored. But laws on their own would not work without a strong back up of education.

It becomes clear that the first step in addressing the problem should be a governmental mass education and information campaign to raise awareness at all levels of society — professionals, rich and poor, the old and young, religious bodies, excisors, etc. — with regard to the health problems associated with the practice, which should stress that FGM is not required by any religion. Although the primary health care system in most of the affected countries does not cover the whole population, it is an avenue for education and child monitoring.

TABLE 1

Estimated prevalence of female genital mutilation in Africa

Country	Estimated population in millions (female)	Estimated % of women and girls operated on
Somalia	4.9	98%
Djibouti	0.3	98%
Sierra Leone	2.3	90%
Ethiopia	27.6	85%
Eritrea	1.75	80%
Sudan	14.1	89% (North)
Mali	4.55	80%
Gambia	0.55	79%
Burkina Faso	5.05	70%
Chad	3.25	60%
Guinea	3.2	60%
Egypt	26.0	55%
Kenya	13.5	50%
Liberia	1.45	50%
Mauritania	1.15	50%
Nigeria	57.85	40%
Ivory Coast	6.95	40%
Guinea Bissau	0.55	40%
Benin	2.65	30%
Ghana	8.45	30%
Togo	2.15	30%
Niger	4.4	20%
Senegal	4.1	20%
Cameroon	6.55	15%
Central African Republic	1.55	10%
Tanzania	14.9	10%
Uganda	9.9	5%

● Sudan is the only country with reliable prevalence data. Other estimates are based on small scale studies and anecdotal information.
● Estimated number of woman and girls who have undergone female genital mutilation in Africa = 109.75 million
● According to *The Progress of Nations*, a report published by UNICEF in 1994, twelve nations in the world have estimated maternal mortality rates

Estimated number (millions)	Maternal mortality (per 100,000 births)	Adult literacy rates as % of males
4.8	1,100	58
0.29	NA	NA
2.07	450	35
23.46	560	48
1.4	NA	NA
9.22	550	28
3.64	2000	59
0.43	1050	NA
3.53	810	32
1.95	960	43
1.92	800	37
14.3	270	54
6.75	170	74
0.72	NA	58
0.57	NA	45
23.14	800	65
2.78	NA	60
0.22	700	48
0.79	160	50
2.53	1000	73
0.43	420	55
0.88	700	43
0.82	600	48
0.98	430	64
0.15	800	48
1.49	340	NA
0.49	300	56

of 800 or more. Nine of these are in the areas in Africa where FGM is wide-ly practised. The average maternal mortality rates for Western Europe is six.
● Information source: Credit to Fran P. Hosken for the original estimates of prevalence of FGM in Africa. All other information is from *Africa Today*, Population Concern, 1994, *The State of the World's Children*, UNICEF, 1994 and *Maternal Mortality, A Global Factbook*, WHO, 1991.

A mass education campaign of this sort needs to be well planned and sustained over a long period and will therefore require resources and technical input. Since most African countries are strapped for cash, this may be difficult. This is the area where the international financial assistance and goodwill will be most appreciated. WHO, UNICEF and other UN Specialized Agencies have declared their willingness to help and we would like to see concrete action in this area.

Local responses to FGM: the empowerment model

FGM does not operate in a socio-cultural and economic vacuum and even armed with knowledge many poor women may still find it difficult to break away from the overt patriarchy which dominates their lives. By focusing purely on mass information campaigns which raise the awareness of people to the health dangers associated with FGM we may not fully meet the needs of rural and poor women. Another lesson from campaigns to combat FGM in Africa is that the elite are breaking away from the practice. The reason often cited for this change is the education of women. Educated urban women are not under the same social pressures: for example they may not be living with the extended families and will therefore have more autonomy in making decisions on the well-being of their girls. Also, their daughters are more likely to marry into a similarly educated social class where conservative attitudes towards women, e.g., insistence on FGM may be slightly modified. We need to focus on the rural, poor and uneducated women if we are to empower them to take control over their health, their bodies and their sexuality.

In order to develop an effective local response to FGM in any given area it is important to develop an analytical framework to understand why the practice persists, and thus to avoid the standard responses to the practice of FGM, which is clearly a multi-dimensional issue.[8] Table 2 shows the multiplicity of factors which might be sustaining FGM at grassroots level.

Rural and poor women are caught up in this multi-complex, and as mentioned before even when they are armed with knowledge, they find that they cannot do very much to stop FGM. So what should be done?

TABLE 2
How female genital mutilation is sustained at grassroots level

SOURCE: The author

The next step might be to work creatively to address the different aspects of the problem. One person or one group will not be able to deal with all the areas involved. Some of the issues that must be confronted, e.g., having a choice, access to resources in the community which will be in male hands, are long term and may be out of our hands. FGM prevention will need to be introduced into the widest possible agendas. For example, we may seek to make sure that all development programmes in the area have a gender perspective so that gradually the balance of economic power becomes more equal, giving women more access to resources. Equally, literacy campaigns will in the long term help to broaden grassroots women's perspective. These are long-term plans, and some suggestions for short-term measures are given below.

Holistic health activities

FGM persists due to gender power imbalance which is played out in cultural norms and values, which are legitimized by an ideology that preserves the gender power imbalance in favour of men.[9] To confront this imbalance directly is to ask for trouble but one can work sensitively, gradually and at grassroots level through a holistic health promotion framework directed at women and men in a community to start equalizing power in an area.

Space for women and girls

The key to empowering grassroots women is to find space within their busy schedules for individual or group work activities to address issues such as how the body functions; sex education to inform them about their sex organs; their functions and what happens when they are mutilated; consciousness-raising to break down the patriarchal myths which have been used to terrorize them into submission (e.g., if the clitoris touches the head of the baby the baby will die, or if the man enters the woman and his penis touches the clitoris the man will die, or women are not pure and cannot even pray unless they are mutilated, etc.).

In group work or individual one-to-one contact it is possible to address issues such as the sanctions meted out to women for not undergoing FGM. The women themselves may come up with their own ideas on the type of support systems needed to address some of the problems they face if they do not submit their daughters to genital mutilation and other forms of gender-based violence. They may want to call on others, e.g. a respected elder, a male-feminist religious leader (there may be one feminist male religious leader in the community) to intervene on their behalf. Doctors, nurses and teachers are respected in many African rural communities. Many will be prepared to act as advocates on behalf of women and girls.

One-to-one work, e.g., by health professionals with families – older women and men explaining and clarifying health issues and supporting the family – might just do the trick.

This is demonstrated in this story:[10]

Rora Habab is a mountain plateau accessible only through deep stony valleys and winding mountain roads after a journey of some 14 hours from the Sudan, and then another 10 hours from northern Eritrea.

The Muslim population of about 12,000 people has traditionally been semi-nomadic, spending the winter months in Rora, and then, as water grows scarce with the coming of summer, travelling with their animals to Sudan and to the north-eastern coast for grazing.

As pastoralists living in the remote high mountains and with little contact with different ideas, they practised female genital mutilation.

Assefash Gulbet, a nurse midwife, worked out of the Rora Health Centre, which is now part of the health service of Eritrea. When she started work there in 1983, she found many severely malnourished women and children. Epidemics occurred because of poor hygiene and most of the women suffered infections as a result of genital mutilation. She started to visit women in their homes, individually, to learn about their problems. At first they were ashamed to tell her their intimate problems.

Assefash talked to the women individually and then later groups came together. Gradually Assefash started to gain their confidence through basic health education. She learnt that they did not want to be pregnant every year and that they suffered a lot of pain as a result of their infibulation.

The women said that nothing would change for them if men did not change their attitudes. They asked her to talk to the men. Assefash had no hesitation in doing so. She discussed with men intimate details of the sexual and gynaecological problems caused by female genital mutilation. The men were at first embarrassed to discuss such things with a strange woman. Assefash made them realize that FGM had just become ritual. The men admitted that they would not know whether a woman had been stitched on the labia or elsewhere.

As a result of these persuasive discussions, no girl child in Rora has been mutilated since 1985.

Assefash and her colleagues at the Rora Health Centre succeeded through a slow process of getting to know these remote communities gaining their trust and showing them the damage of the customary practice of female genital mutilation.

Where should a young girl go for help if she realizes that there is an impending genital mutilation? Which adult should she talk to in a village whom she is sure will support her? Can women come together to tackle the bride price? What are women and girls' constitutional rights and how do they access this at grassroots level? In some African countries women lawyers are offering a voluntary service, helping such women to gain access to their constitutional rights. These are questions which grassroots women's health groups should be considering.

Concepts of womanhood are socially constructed. If for centuries women have been conditioned to see mutilation of their genitals as a necessary part of womanhood, then they will need space to deal with the pain of redefinition of self. This can be addressed through one-to-one or group counselling activities. Health group facilitators will need to develop counselling skills.

What should be done with rituals of passage? Can one manip-ulates rites of passage to enhance girls, sense of themselves with-out mutilation? Instead of girls being conditioned to accept their subservient role in society, girls can be given assertiveness train-ing, sex education, etc., within puberty rites. The excisors may work with us if given alternative income and a central role to play in women's health activity.

All these group activities can be undertaken in the women's groups which already exist in every area.

Space for men

Although the practice of FGM operates within women's sphere, it is performed for male benefit. Generally, men sit on the fence, pretending that FGM is a women's issue and has nothing to do with them. They need to be approached by health professionals, social workers, as well as other men sympathetic to the anti-FGM campaign, to be given sex education, and to raise awareness of the health consequences of FGM and its implications for child-birth and sexual health. Some are beginning to understand that it is pleasurable for men to enjoy sex with women who have not undergone genital mutilation and that sexual bonding within a relationship consolidates it. Couples will definitely need sexual counselling. Some men and women in the community can be trained to support the campaign in this area.

Men will need to be persuaded to acknowledge that female children are not only a mother's responsibility but the responsi-bility of both parents. They need to be supported to speak out publicly against FGM. Many men are misinformed about women's sexuality and may feel threatened by losing their power over women. They need to be reassured and counselled to see the eradication of FGM as a development issue for both men and women. No country can develop when half its population is kept in chains!

Religion

FGM has no firm foundation in religion but is used by chauvin-ist religious men to control women. Religious men who can influence attitudes should be central to the education campaign. Feminists religious scholars should be able to support the campaign by speaking to women and to religious leaders.

Case study from Egypt

Dr Maurice Assad, an educationalist, first raised the issue of FGM through the Coptic Church in 1978. The Coptic Church then initiated the programme 'Family Life and Family Planning' to address FGM and surrounding issues that perpetuate the practice. The Care of Girls Committee was formed to address FGM by challenging the subservient role of young Egyptian girls, and accepting their dignity and integrity and by advocating and supporting greater equality for women and girls. The project was headed by Mrs Hedy Banoub of the diocese of Beni Suef. The project workers realized that it was not enough to educate people about the harmful effects of FGM, since FGM was tightly interwoven with the submissive status of girls. They therefore raised wider issues of unfair treatment of women, for example, marriage 'defloration' — checking the genitals of a young woman at marriage to make sure her hymen is intact; breaking the hymen and showing a blood-stained towel to the public as a proof of her virginity. 'In many instances, the father kills his daughter if there is no blood shown on this towel,' says Mrs Banoub.

According to members of the Committee, one of the problems in attempting to promote the rights of girls in Egypt is the fact that the girls have very low self-esteem. In many cases, when a baby girl is born, she is unwelcome, even to her parents. This inevitably affects her self-esteem as she grows up. Girls also observe how their brothers receive more attention. Mrs Banoub says that girls are also reminded that they are the less favoured children by the lack of care shown towards their important life events. For example, when a girl begins to menstruate, no-one explains to her that this will happen. It therefore becomes an alarming event.

Girls also grow up with an expectation of the horror of genital mutilation. 'Girls in the village tremble as they grow,' says Mrs Banoub. 'They have seen that an older sister has suffered, or heard about the experiences of other girls in the neighbourhood. As a result, first there is fear, and then the appalling memory of the experience. Some girls live with a phobia that one or the other parent will kill them. This fear can remain even in adulthood'.

Another problem that faces girls is that they are forced to marry men chosen for them at a very young age. They have few rights in adult life, and the law and customs relating to inheritance discriminate against them.

Mrs Banoub believes that an important first step in establishing the rights of girls is to stop the practice of treating them as inferior to boys. She believes that both discrimination, and female genital mutilation, should be seen as harmful habits that need to be broken. 'Some of our customs and habits date back to ancient times', she says, 'but that does not mean that they are not harmful'.

Street theatre

In order to encourage discussion of these issues, the Care for Girls Committee has commissioned plays, picture books, posters, slide-shows and audio tapes. They have brought together numerous groups of church and other religious and community leaders as well as health and social workers for formal consultations. At each of these meetings, one of the plays is presented and copies of the books are distributed as an integral part of the programme.

The Committee has also arranged many local meetings in villages of Upper and Lower Egypt. The visits to villages normally begin with a performance of one the plays lasting almost 30 minutes, followed by a one-hour discussion with the audience. Representatives of the Committee then work individually with different groups in order to maximize the impact of their message. For example, one may work with local leaders while another talks to the girls themselves.

Work in the villages includes home visits. Here, family members are able to describe the pressures on them to conform to the practice of allowing their daughters to be circumcised for fear that an uncircumcised girl will not find a husband. According to Dr Maurice Assad there have recently been stories of men who have refused to marry uncircumcised women.

Mrs Banoub, however, is confident that there are also examples of positive attitude changes. 'I know of a family in which there are four daughters', she says. 'The elder two daughters were circumcised. Then, the mother learned that female circumcision was harmful and has refused to circumcise her youngest two daughters.' Mrs Banoub says that although there was considerable pressure from the mother-in-law and other women in the family to have her two younger daughters circumcised, the mother refused.[11]

INITIATIVES AND ACTIVITIES WITHIN COUNTRIES

West Africa

BENIN
In Benin, FGM, which is practised mainly in the northern part of the country. The Benin National Committee is the national chapter of the Inter-African Committee (IAC) and was formed in 1991 by Mrs Isabelle Teveodjre, the former co-ordinator of the NGO Working Group on Traditional Practices, with the assistance of a Peace Corps volunteer. The group based their work on a 30-year-old law which protects the integrity of the human body.

In 1983 IAC Benin carried out a survey in Atacora funded by the American Embassy in Cotonou. Activities have intensified since 1990. The National Committee has set about training rural animators and sending them into the villages, organizing seminars for religious and community leaders, mayors, doctors, midwives, social workers and representatives of youth and women's organizations. The National Committee also collaborates with the Ministry of Social Affairs and Health and the government of Benin permits the distribution of posters and educational materials in government-run clinics.

BURKINA FASO
The early Roman Catholic missionaries threatened to excommunicate their converts who practised excision. This did not work. From 1960 onwards the first President of Upper Volta (now Burkina Faso) promoted an awareness campaign. This also did not work.

At the 1979 Khartoum WHO seminar, Alice Tiendregeogon

spoke on behalf of the Women's Federation of Upper Volta, later to become the Women's Federation of Burkina. Although infibulation is not practised in Burkina Faso, the attempted suppression of excision in all forms met with strong resistance from a population which is 30 per cent Muslim, 20 per cent Catholic and 50 per cent Animist. The campaign against excision, launched in 1975 and using the radio (the only way of reaching remote areas) in all the vernacular languages, provoked such hostile reactions that it had to be discontinued.

A survey was carried out and in answer to the question 'Why do you practise female circumcision?' all Muslim men replied that it was their religion, whereas non-Muslims and Catholics gave various reasons, custom, hygiene, supposed sterility of the non-excised women, immorality 'a non-excised women goes with a man...' The women, with the exception of a minority of teachers, nurses, doctors and 'modern' midwives, replied that just as their mother were excised, so they had to follow the same path.

Thus, in Burkina Faso, a decision was made to approach the eradication of excision as purely a medical problem, conferring on a gynaecologist the task of exposing the physical complications of excision, of explaining that excision does not necessarily remove sexual desire in a woman, and that a non-excised woman is in no way automatically immoral.

In 1985, during the national women's week, a proposal to abolish excision was put forward. By this time, people, particularly in urban areas, were speaking openly about excision. In 1988 a national seminar on excision was organized. This received media coverage and raised awareness among the people. In 1990 it was decided that the time was ripe to set up an institutional framework for the eradication of excision. The National Committee for the Fight Against the Practice of Excision (CNLPE) was set up. This Committee, which is affiliated to the IAC, has a mandate to develop action against all forms of harmful practices affecting the health and the full development of women and children. It has the responsibility to develop, co-ordinate and evaluate action for the abolition of excision and has the strong support of the government as well as of UNICEF, UNFPA the UN Centre for Human Rights.

The National Committee has representatives from various government ministries, NGOs, feminist associations, professional bodies, and some religious organizations including traditional authorities. Its president is the First Lady, Mrs Chantal Compaore, and the vice president is Mrs Heldring Frauke, wife of the ambassador of the Netherlands.

The National Committee is decentralized and has nine provincial committees, which collaborate with professionals, wives of leaders, entertainers, social agents, health workers and teachers who then spread the information to different fields.

In 1991 the National Committee made a film entitled *My Daughter Will Not Be Excised*, funded by WHO, USAID and other donors. The film is shown periodically in local theatres.

CAMEROON
Female genital mutilation continues to be practised in some areas of the far north and south west. The IAC Cameroon chapter was created in 1992 and aims to eradicate all traditional practices affecting the health of women and children. In order to reach this goal, IAC Cameroon has developed a programme of activities for 1992 including sensitization of governmental and international bodies as well as local women's associations. IAC Cameroon is invited to all meetings organized by the Ministry of Social Welfare and Women's Affairs, the Ministry of Public Health and by women's organizations. Research projects on female genital mutilation in Cameroon have been approved by USAID but funds have not yet been allocated.

CHAD
Female genital mutilation is widespread and performed on females at a young age. According to the 1993 US Department of State's human rights report to Congress, FGM is deeply rooted in tradition, both in the north and south, and is strongly advocated by many Chadians, women as well as men. The US Agency for International Development funded a survey in Moyen Chari Préfecture which showed that the percentage of women who have undergone FGM is extremely high. Some 96 per cent of rural Catholic women in Moyen Chari were found to be excised as

compared to 86 per cent Animist, 80 per cent of Protestant and 55 per cent of Muslim women. Urban statistics range from a low 53 per cent for Protestant women to 63 per cent for Muslims, 75 per cent for Animists and 86 per cent for Catholics. Until 1993 there was no governmental action to prohibit FGM.

GAMBIA

In 1981, the Gambian Nurses Association organized a seminar on the practice of FGM. In 1985 a study on FGM in the Gambia sponsored by FORWARD/Oxfam and undertaken by the Gambian Women's Bureau, showed that over 70 per cent of Gambian females undergo FGM. Among certain ethnic groups, e.g. the Fulas and the Serahules, the incidence is 100 per cent. Excision is the most common type practised but about seven per cent of girls undergo some type of infibulation. The former government of the Gambia recognized FGM as a harmful practice which needed to be abolished through education. In its national population policy for socio-economic development it called for action to reduce the incidence of FGM.

Except for the Foni District and in the western division, the Gambian National Committee on Traditional Practices (GAMCO-TRAP), a national chapter of the IAC, has successfully completed a series of sensitization and awareness-creating programmes on female genital mutilation and on harmful practices such as early childhood marriage and nutritional taboos throughout the Gambia.

Women were brought together and given training on how to sensitize the general public to the harmful effects of FGM. Traditional Birth Attendants, many of whom were excisors, were told of the health effects of FGM. Information campaigns were directed at women, community leaders, youth and children. These activities were carried out with the participation of the Ministry of Health Family Planning Association and the Ministry of Education, Youth, Sports and Culture. Religious and community leaders were encouraged to speak about Islam and FGM.

BAFROW (Foundation for Research on Women's Health, Productivity and the Environment) is another Gambian women's organization established to carry out action-orientated research, surveys and pilot projects, on issues related to women's health, women's productivity and the environment. Its ultimate objective is to support institutions and agencies and, in particular, indigenous grassroots women's groups, in developing educational programmes to be implemented in collaboration with relevant government ministries and local NGOs. A pilot programme has been developed with funding support from Population Action International and technical assistance from FORWARD. It aims to address FGM in multi-dimensional ways through community health promotion, restructuring of puberty rituals and alternative income for excisors. The programme which is co-funded by UK Overseas Development Organization through FORWARD, will start early 1995.

Rose Bojang, a Scottish woman married to a Gambian, works in her village to raise awareness on FGM and runs a holistic health clinic in Banjul. She came back home one day to find that two of her step-daughters had undergone excision and went into a state of shock. Whilst in England she collected education materials, including four videos from FORWARD, pamphlets, WHO packs on FGM and these have started the questioning process for women in the village. Recently they watched the documentary 'Warrior Marks' (produced by Alice Walker and Pratibha Parmar in 1993) and realized for the first time that the practice of FGM, which they thought was their own little secret, was known to the whole world.

GHANA
FGM is practised by some ethnic groups in the northern part of Ghana. Early Christian missionaries in the north of Ghana discouraged FGM among their converts. This had some impact on the educated elite. The National Council on Women and Development started to collect information on FGM in the early 1980s and the Ghanaian Association on Women's Welfare (GAWW) established in 1984, which is the IAC Ghana chapter, undertook two studies on FGM in the Upper East Region of Ghana with funding support from Forward International. The results showed that in the Upper East and Upper West Region of Ghana, 75-85 per cent of girls have undergone excision. In Southern Ghana,

FGM is prevalent among migrants from Upper East and Upper West Regions of Ghana, Mali, Togo, Niger, Burkina Faso and other neighbouring countries where the practice is widespread.

GAWW has undertaken advocacy work with the government which has resulted in the inclusion in the country's constitution of a clause stating that all customary practices which dehumanize the person, both physically and mentally, be abolished, and the promulgation of by-laws by chiefs and members of district assemblies in five districts in the Upper East Region. GAWW has gained the support of the First Lady of Ghana.

GAWW has undertaken educational programmes aimed at sensitizing the different target groups to the hazards of harmful traditional practices, through seminars, workshops and group discussions. This has led to increased awareness of the health hazards surrounding FGM. It has also organized training for TBAs, and collaborates with government ministries, international NGOs and local NGOs. National legislation prohibiting FGM was passed in June 1994. Since that time, the National Council of Women and Development (the government Ministry of Women's Affairs) in collaboration with GAWW, the 31st December Women's Movement and the Ministry of Health have launched a two-year programme of anti-FGM education.

GUINEA

The Co-ordinating body on Traditional Practices Affecting the Health of Women and Children (CPTAFE) is the Guinean branch of the Inter-African Committee. CPTAFE was created in 1988 as a non-governmental organization and is recognized by the government of Guinea. CPTAFE collaborates with international organizations, other NGOs and the government through the Department of Health and Social Affairs and Women's Affairs and indirectly through all other ministry departments.

Through the advocacy work of CPTAFE, an article has already been included in the Guinean constitution which upholds the right to physical integrity of the human person and condemns all forms of inhuman treatment. CPTAFE has produced four films on female circumcision, as well as brochures and leaflets, and radio and TV programmes in the form of debates and lectures; it has organized seminars for sensitization, information and training for journalists, religious leaders, health professionals and TBAs. The wife of Guinea's president has participated in the activities sponsored by CPTAFE, and actively works to bring an end to FGM in Guinea.

One of the most active Americans in the fight against the practice of FGM in Guinea is a young Peace Corps volunteer, Connie Hedrington, who works in a health centre in the remote village of Doko in the region of Upper Guinea. She became concerned about FGM after seeing a young patient die as a result of the operation. She wrote for education material from FORWARD and other organizations. She has researched the practice in her area, written papers on the subject, and conducted educational sessions for villagers in the local language, Malinke. She reports that some infibulation is practised in Guinea, which was one of the African countries which sponsored the World Health Assembly resolution for the elimination of harmful health practices including FGM (May 1993).

GUINEA-BISSAU
FGM is still a widespread practice among the Fulas and the Mandinkas and it occurs at a young age. The National Association of Women has undertaken some small-scale surveys which showed that all Muslim women have undergone female genital mutilation. In 1992, the government supported a regional seminar organized by the Guinea-Bissau chapter of the Inter-African Committee. This raised public awareness about FGM. It has been discussed on TV and two seminars have been held in the eastern region, where there is a large Muslim population and at the Ministère de la Promotion Féminine. FGM continues, however, despite official prohibition and education campaigns.

IVORY COAST
Female genital mutilation is widespread among a number of ethnic groups. In 1987 the Department of Gynaecology and Obstetrics undertook a study and found that out of 4,935 deliveries registered, a fifth of the women had undergone excision. Excision is practised in the north, north-eastern and western parts of

the country. In March, 1994 several Ivorian newspapers ran stories on two Ivorian girls, aged 16 and 6, who went into a coma after FGM was performed by a woman in the village. The US Embassy in Abidjan supports the activities of the International Movement of Democratic Women (MIFED), a non-partisan NGO based in Côte d'Ivoire, which focuses on a variety of civic and women's issues. One of MIFED's objectives is the elimination of female genital mutilation. The group has organized seminars and other events to educate Ivorians about the effects of the practice.

The IAC National Committee was formed in 1992. Four sub-committees have been set up to fight against female circumcision or incision, early marriage and practices related to childbirth. These sub-committees cover four municipalities in Abidjan where the population adheres to these practices. Each committee is composed of at least fifteen members. In collaboration with the Ministry of Women's affairs (through its urban and rural animators) the Ministry of Health and Social Affairs (through doctors, midwives and nurses of the MCH Centres), the activities of the sub-committees consist of carrying out programmes of sensitization and distribution of information on the health hazards of such practices, within different existing structures of the communities such as youth centres, educational institutes for women, maternity hospitals, MCH Centres. The media, especially radio and TV, are used to further sensitization and to stimulate debates.

MALI
The Centre Djoliba, set up in 1964, is a private body which assembles youth and women for various educational purposes. Its women's programme includes health information on FGM. In 1984 the Comité Malien de Lutte Contres Les Practiques Traditionnelles Néfastes (COMAPRAT) was established under the umbrella of the Union Nationale des Femmes du Mali (UNFM). COMAPRAT undertook information, sensitization and training programmes in collaboration with other NGOs in Bamako and Koulikoro. The group also organized workshops for midwives, opinion leaders, religious leaders and the press. In 1990, following a change of government, COMAPRAT was dissolved along

with UNFM. A new association, AMSOPT, has been formed, and has undertaken training of youth and has organized a sensitization and information seminar for religious and traditional leaders in the six regions of Mali. It has also held a one-day meeting for reflection with cultural counsellors from Iraq, Iran, Kuwait, Saudi Arabia, Algeria and Morocco, as well as with religious associations in Mali.

AMSOPT has undertaken a sensitization project for eighteen excisors and their assistants. The objective is to use these women in the different communities in order to involve them in the fight and also to initiate income-generating activities for them. The media are involved in the campaign, as well: two private radio stations 'Kaira' and 'Freedom' have organized a Gallup poll on FGM and on the case of the Gambian woman who was sentenced to five years imprisonment in France for performing female genital mutilation.

NIGER

The Nigerien Comite (CONIPRAT) was established in 1990 and has conducted a survey on traditional practices which shows that FGM is practised by the Peuhl, Songhai, Kourtey and the Wogo. The study recommended the organization of a national seminar to disseminate the findings, and further workshops and TV programmes on traditional practices.

CONIPRAT has distributed the results of the study among concerned agencies, professional and international organizations. It has organized sensitization seminars and workshops. It is represented at all national seminars organized by national agencies having the same objectives. It also uses the media and plans to develop sub-committees in eight regions, and has drawn up a three-year plan of action.

NIGERIA

When Esther Ogunmodede, a Nigerian journalist, began questioning the practice, she sought out other Nigerian women who, like herself, had undergone genital mutilation. Her enquiries showed that several excisions took place in Nigeria every year and it was a widely practised tradition. She began to write and speak out against the custom in the 1970s.

A 1983 study by Dr Oduntan and Dr Modupe showed that the prevalence of FGM ranged from 15-100 per cent depending on ethnic group. In 1985-6 the National Association of Nigerian Nurses and Midwives (NANNM) conducted a survey of female genital mutilation practices in all nineteen states. The study showed that FGM was practised in thirteen states and in five states an estimated 90 per cent of women underwent some type of genital mutilation. In the state of Kaduna 15 per cent of women were infibulated, 45 per cent were excised and 35 per cent were circumcised. From 1988-90 the members of this professional association carried out a nationwide campaign to eradicate harmful traditional practices that included female genital mutilation, child marriage and nutritional taboos. With financial support from Population Action International and technical assistance from PATH (Programme in Appropriate Technology for Health) NANNM conducted a programme that started with national workshops in Lagos. Following this eleven workshops were held in states chosen for their high rate of harmful traditional practices. Communication strategies were designed after NANNM members had conducted focus group discussions and learned some of the reasons for the underlying attitude to the practices.

The first phase focused on training trainers who, in turn, conducted training and educational activities at state and community levels. Drama, market promotions and community mobilization and educational campaigns carried the message of the harmful effects of FGM. The nurses also used newspapers and electronic media to disseminate their message. The Project Director appeared in a national television talk show and other local NANNM leaders appeared on radio broadcasts. Articles about this previously taboo subject appeared in national newspapers. The project stimulated an open discussion about the topic.

In 1984, a Nigerian National Committee, a national chapter of the Inter-African Committee, was also set up to fight against FGM. The Committee has obtained collaboration and support from the honourable Ministers, Commissioners and Chairmen in the Ministries of Health, Education and Information and this has assisted their activities and enhanced the trust of the masses.

The Training, Information, Education, Communication (TIEC)

seminar/workshop was an effective strategy in creating aware-ness among the populace. Through this medium, people from all walks of life were sensitized, with a reasonable proportion mobi-lized to continue the campaign at the grassroots level. The youth and school children, who are the future policy-makers, and par-ents, were not left out. Lectures and discussions, various teach-ing materials, video film on FGM, and the mass media were used to disseminate the necessary information. The Committee has undertaken training of the TBAs and traditional healers. It has upgraded their knowledge and skills so that they will be better informed on safe motherhood. The Nigerian National Commit-tee publishes a newsletter *Your Task* on traditional practices.

Nigeria was one of the five African countries which sponsored a resolution at the forty-sixth World Health Assembly, calling for the elimination of harmful health practices, including female genital mutilation. The Federal Ministry of Health sponsors public aware-ness and education projects to inform communities about the health hazards associated with female genital mutilation.

SENEGAL
In 1981 CAMS (Campaign Pour L'Abolition des Mutilations Sex-uelles) was formed in Paris with Awa Thiam as the President and a branch organization 'Femmes Et Société' in Senegal. CAMS-International was later based in Senegal. CAMS takes a gender perspective approach in addressing FGM. Its original aim was to galvanize a grassroots feminist women's movement in Fran-cophone West Africa. This has not been possible due to lack of resources and poor organization.

From 1982 it has mobilized and organized seminars on FGM and violence against women. It set up a gender research unit on women at the University of Dakar and published and distrib-uted in Francophone Africa, the feminist newsletter *Femmes Et Société*. The publication has collapsed as a result of financial dif-ficulties.

In 1988 a survey on FGM was carried out by ENDA Environ-mental Development Action in the Third World (ENDA Tiers-Monde) with support from the Inter-African Committee. FGM was found to be most common among the Muslim population and is practised most widely through the eastern region of the country where it affects the general population. In 1992 the Senegalese Committee on Traditional Practices (COSEPRAT), the Inter-African Committee national chapter in Senegal, organized jointly with ENDA a seminar for Muslim leaders in the Casamance region with the participation of excisors and certain leaders and the Ministry for Women, Children and Family.

COSEPRAT collaborates with the government and the Prime Minister opened their seminar. It also collaborates with UNFPA, WHO and, to a certain extent, UNICEF. The group's activities include radio broadcasts which reach a large number of the population, medical research and participation in a youth seminar organized by the Scouts and Associations for the Well-Being of the Family (AIBEF).

SIERRA LEONE

Except among the Creoles who live round Freetown, excision is widely practised in Sierra Leone within a strong ritualistic context and is at the core of rites of passage of girls from childhood to womanhood and within traditional power bases for women known as 'secret societies'. These societies are shrouded in secrecy and taboo and have evolved a magical and supernatural aura. Girls are taken in age sets to undergo the rites of passage. Members swear oaths not to reveal information on the secret society and breaking this oath brings recriminations to the person. Membership of the secret society, only open to those women who undergo the rites of passage, confers on a person adult status and the right to be a member of the community and to participate in the society. Girls are said to be given skills to prepare them to be wives, co-wives, mothers and members of the community. Non-members are regarded as children and outcasts within society. They are not allowed to take up leadership roles, e.g. political office, in their community and will not receive the support needed for their economic survival. Age sets who are excised together benefit from life-long bonds of sisterhood and enjoy mutual support, particularly in times of crisis, and approval from society. Women who run the secret societies are revered, feared and deemed to possess supernatural powers. They earn income, in cash and kind, from the excision ceremonies.

Much fear surrounds the practice of FGM. Open criticism of the 'secret society' can evoke threats, including death threats. Men who criticize the society openly might be threatened with castration and women non-members with forced excision. The 'secret society' draws support from members of the influential elite who are members themselves or have relatives as members. Excision is practised by all classes, including the educated elite. Sierra Leoneans who live abroad bring their daughters home to undergo the rites of passage. Children who come of age in the community and are not excised can be forcibly seized to undergo FGM.

The Sierra Leone Association on Women's Welfare (SIAWW) a national chapter of the Inter-Africa Committee, was set up in 1984. A survey carried out by Dr Olayinka Koso-Thomas between 1982 and 1986 showed the prevalence of FGM to be 95 per cent. The survey became the basis of her book *The Circumcision of Women: A Strategy for Eradication*[12] which is the first book on excision to come out of Anglophone West Africa. SIAWW has taken a very cautious approach and has initiated sensitization activities. There is now discussion on FGM within educated circles – doctors, midwives, nurses, journalists, teachers and among students.

Although SIAWW has undertaken a strong advocacy role with governmental bodies, it has not been able to secure the support of the governmental machinery. It has secured collaboration from UNICEF, WHO and other NGOs, associations and religious bodies, and is currently undertaking WHO-funded research on 'The influence of female genital mutilation on contraceptive choice.'

TOGO

FGM exists in Tchaoudjo region in the north of Togo. In 1984 a National Committee of the Inter-African Committee was formed with the support of the Ministry of Social Affairs. Between 1984-90 the Committee organized seminars and workshops to sensitize excisors, health workers, policy-makers and village women and men in the Tchaoudjo region.

CARE/Togo has a reproductive health care project that is just beginning in the Savanna (the northern most area of Togo) which is said to be an affected area. CARE is attempting to determine the extent of the practice before designing strategies to address FGM.

Togo sponsored the World Health Assembly May 1993 resolution on harmful traditional practices.

East Africa

KENYA
In 1979, Mrs Eddah Gachukia, one of five women Members of Parliament at the time, was actively engaged through the National Council of Women of Kenya in efforts to combat mutilation. She described the situation in Kenya at the time as one in which little or no concrete work or research has been carried out. The National Council of Women of Kenya appealed to various agencies, including the International Council of Women, UNICEF and the World Health Organization, for a grant to enable Kenyan women scholars and gynaecologists from the areas in which female genital mutilation was practised, to carry out reliable studies which the Council could use to obtain government support for the discouragement (if not banning) of the practice. The leaders of the National Christian Council of Kenya also called for research into the practice.

Mrs Gachukia stressed that in most parts of Kenya, female genital mutilation was accepted voluntarily. She saw the problem as an educational one and advocated the expansion of girls' education as an alternative means of achieving self-identity rather than by legislating against FGM. It was important to educate women, both mothers and girls, as to the medical complications and their consequences. Mrs Gachukia felt that international propaganda was not helpful at the national level, especially when this was highly coloured by prejudice, alarmist, and based on erroneous information. International organizations and genuinely informed individuals, she declared, should support local effort and expertise.

From 1982, attempts were made by the Women's Action Group on Excision and Infibulation (WAGFEI), formed under the auspices of Minority Rights Group, to secure funding for research. These efforts were not taken up, and few individuals and groups undertook action in this area. However, the National Council of Women of Kenya accepted a small grant from WAGFEI to promote education. Another group which took action is the West Pokot Women's Project in Kapenguria run by Mrs Margaret Limakori and Mrs Dinah Katina. With funding support from Radda Barnen (Save The Children, Sweden), this project has gone from strength to strength. For more than a decade Mrs Limakori and Mrs Katina have focused their energies at grassroots level working with their people, persuading and encouraging parents to abandon FGM in the community. They have had a certain degree of success in the prevention of FGM in Kapenguria.

In 1990 the Kenyan National Committee on Traditional Practices was formed. It planned to carry out a statistical study on the number of women excised and the ethnic groups which continue with the practice, hoping to use this information as a basis for specific research.

In 1991, Maendeleo Ya Wanawake (MYWO) the largest grassroots women's NGO in Kenya, (with membership of over 2 million), which was established in 1952 to enhance the welfare of women and their families, decided to address this issue. In order to find out about the knowledge, attitudes and practices of Kenyan women regarding traditional practices affecting the health of women and children, i.e. female genital mutilation, nutritional taboos and early marriage, MYWO conducted survey research in four districts of Kenya where these practices are believed to be widely practised: Meru, Kisii, Narok and Samburu. MYWO worked with PATH/Nairobi, who assisted them in the development of the quantitive survey and trained enumerators in interpersonal communication and interviewing techniques.

The findings indicate that 90 per cent of women in four districts have undergone FGM, predominantly *sunna* in Kissi, excision in Meru and Narok, and infibulation in Samburu. FGM was performed on girls between the ages of 8-13. They are performed by a traditional excisor in the village, or in the bush. It was found that 90 per cent of the excisions were done in a group setting, with 71 per cent of the excisors using the same instrument for many girls without cleaning it between procedures.

Sixty-five per cent of women interviewed wanted excision to continue, stating that changes are unwanted and could be difficult to bring about; 81 per cent stated that FGM was 'good tradition' and 68 per cent stated that it was 'a sign of maturity'. Only 35 per cent favoured discontinuation of FGM saying that it is against 'religious teaching' and 'human dignity'. A project development workshop was held in March 1992 to disseminate the research findings to MYWO members, government officials and the international community.

TANZANIA

FGM is practised in the following regions: Dodoma, Singida, Arusha, Kilimanjaro and Mara. Partial removal of the labia minora is practised by some tribes in Morogora and Iringa regions. Infibulation is practised by Somali ethnic groups who reside in Arusha region. In 1971 the government of Tanzania launched a campaign in Dodoma and Singida regions, when the prevalence of complications of sepsis, bleeding and deaths alarmed everybody, but this was an emergency measure.

A workshop was held in Dar-es-Salaam in 1986 which came up with a proposal for a campaign for the abolition of FGM. Following the workshop a fact-finding survey on FGM was carried out in 1988-9 by the Women's Section of the Institute of Adult Education. This resulted in the production and distribution of a booklet on FGM, Dangers of Female Circumcision[13] written in Kiswhahili. After this initiative FGM was discussed in several meetings.

In 1992 the Tanzanian chapter of the Inter-African Committee was formed. A project proposal was prepared with the following aims: to undertake three district seminars for government leaders and Members of Parliament, to hold focused group discussions, to initiate action-orientated research to assess the extent of harmful traditional practices, and subsequent seminars and meetings for public mobilization.

UGANDA

In Uganda FGM is only practised in Kapchorwa. In 1990 the Ugandan National Chapter of the Inter-African Committee took up the campaign against FGM in Uganda. According to the group, the politicians from Kapchorwa were afraid to lead a crusade against FGM for fear of losing the support of the community which voted them into power. The IAC National Committee risked going into the district. They managed to win the support of the elders and religious leaders in the community. In 1991, the IAC Uganda was able to hold a one-day seminar with the community leaders, who gave a mandate to the National Committee to come to the district and to conduct sensitization workshops.

Once the group had broken the ice on the subject, the politicians joined them in the campaign. In 1990 they held a two-day sensitization workshop, the first one ever organized at the national level. During the workshop, the district authorities passed a by-law saying that from the time the IAC moved in until further notice, FGM should be optional. Anybody found forcing a girl or a woman to undergo genital mutilation would be punished by law. In 1992 some men were jailed when they tried to force their wives to undergo genital mutilation.

IAC Uganda has carried on holding sensitization workshops for Muslim and Somali women in Uganda. Funding for these activities is provided by the National Association of Women's Organizations in Uganda, UNICEF, UNFPA, the Ministry of Women in Development and the World Bank (Safe Motherhood Initiative).

The Ugandan National Committee collaborates with the Ugandan Women Lawyers' Association (FIDA) which helps them to fight FGM under the Human Rights Act. Other partners are the Safe Motherhood Initiative, the National Association of Women's Organizations in Uganda, the Media Women's Association, which helps with publicity and the Association of Uganda Doctors which offers facilities for workshops. The group works closely with traditional birth attendants, whom they train to campaign against the practice at grassroots level. Government ministries have given them moral and some material help.

North-East and the Horn of Africa

DJIBOUTI

It is estimated that 95 per cent of Djibouti women are infibulated. FGM is entrenched among the Issa and Afars who make up the overwhelming majority of the population of Djibouti. In the early 1980s young women initiated discussions on FGM and called for its abolition. In 1987 a National Committee with members from the Ministries of Health, Justice and Education, as well as from the Red Crescent Society and Union Nationale des Femmes de Djibouti (UNFD) was set up. The Committee works under the umbrella of UNFD. Article 333 of the penal code outlaws the practice of 'Female Circumcision'. The official policy in Djibouti on FGM is to discourage infibulations as a first step towards change. UNFD runs a clinic where girls are brought in for a less radical form of FGM. Circumcision is performed by a traditional excisor. Before the operation the girls are given local anaesthesia. However, a field mission report by the UN Centre for Human Rights to Djibouti in 1991, indicates that this was not successful as the grandmothers took the girls home complaining that the mutilation was incomplete as no infibulation was performed.

UNFD organizes national seminars, workshops, training for traditional birth attendants and information sessions for various target groups, such as religious leaders, mothers, fathers and policy-makers. The Ministry of Health allows the use of clinics and health training centres for diffusion of information about infibulation and other harmful traditional practices. The Ministry of Information encourages wide media coverage of information relating to conferences, seminars and workshops on FGM. The WHO representative in Djibouti, Mrs Edna Ismail, also trains village birth attendants about the dangers of FGM.

EGYPT

In 1979 a ground-breaking seminar entitled 'Bodily Mutilation of Young Females' was held in Cairo. This was presided over by Mrs Aziza Hussein. The seminar brought together representatives of the Arab league, UNICEF, WHO, the Sudanese Embassy, the Egyptian Ministry of Social Affairs, the General Organization of

Information and Medical Departments of the Cairo Governorate and many NGOs, medical faculties and research institutions.

Participants concluded that FGM was a kind of mutilation. It was harmful and therefore it was imperative to confront and oppose it. The operation caused psychological trauma which could affect a girl for the rest of her life. It was not recommended by religious belief and furthermore, there was no scientific evidence to prove any relationship between genital mutilation and a girl's femininity and/or chastity.

A three-year project to implement the resolutions passed at the 1979 seminar was started in October 1982, funded by the Population Crisis Committee (now Population Action International) and by the Cairo Family Planning Association. A co-ordinator was appointed, and a programme initiated which included the production of education materials and training in their use for doctors, nurses, midwives, social workers and similar groups. A similar programme was developed by the Women's Programme of the Bishopric of Public, Ecumenical and Social Services in Cairo, backed by the Coptic Orthodox Church in conjunction with the World Council of Churches.

A study by the co-ordinator, based on interviews conducted among 500 women aged between 20 and 30, found that 80 per cent had undergone genital mutilation. The main reason given was that the old customs and traditions were inherited without questioning from previous generations. On the basis of field experience, an information programme was conducted among educated and uneducated groups. A twelve-member National Committee, affiliated to the Inter-African Committee (IAC), was formed to combat female genital mutilation. Since 1985, it has undertaken public education, concentrating on Mother and Child Health Clinics, family planning centres, and trainers of nursing and social work leaders. It has initiated education for target groups such as secondary school students, young men, female factory workers etc. To reach out to a wider audience it has used the media extensively.

A major focus of the project is lobbying to introduce an explicit law which prohibits female genital mutilation, to replace the Ministry of Health's 1959 decree. This decree reformed the practice by modifying it, and tried to bring the operation into hospitals and surgeries. It has proved woefully ineffective in this aim, and may have had the contrary result of pushing the practice further underground. The National Committee argues that only legal prohibition will be effective.

During the last three years, the greatest effort in raising public awareness has been put into the training and information campaign with the Ministries of Social Welfare, Education, Information and Health, and local governments using their networks to pass on the message. Training has been given to Traditional Birth Attendants in co-operation with UNICEF.

ETHIOPIA

The Revolutionary Ethiopian Women's Association (REWA) has a mandate under the former Mengistu regime to eradicate cultures, customs and practices that deny women their rights. Together with the Ministry of Health, REWA supported action for the eradication of FGM. In 1983 UNICEF funded a study on FGM in Ethiopia which showed that circumcision, excision and infibulation were widely practised throughout the country, with the exception of some ethnic groups such as Begas in Wellga. Circumcision and excision were mostly practised in big towns and in the highlands, but in Muslim areas in the regions adjoining Somalia, girls were infibulated.

Ethiopia's transitional government has expressed interest in enhancing the status of women. It has established a 'Women's Desk' within each ministry and gives moral support to the anti-FGM campaign. The National Committee on Traditional Practices in Ethiopia (NCTPE), a chapter of the IAC, has undertaken a broad range of activities including: the production and distribution of teaching materials, awareness-raising workshops in two-thirds of the country, education activities with Somali refugees and Ethiopia returnees in East Hararge, awareness-raising symposia for the media, awareness-raising in secondary schools and research. These activities have been funded by Radda Barnen, AIDOS, USAID, UNHCR, the Inter-African Committee and the Ministry of Health.

ERITREA

Female genital mutilation is widespread in Eritrea. Circumcision, excision and infibulation are practised by almost all cultural and religious groups in the country.

Prior to independence, the Eritrean People's Liberation Front (EPLF) undertook abolition campaigns in the liberated areas. The EPLF found that the discontinuation of the practice was tied to female education and raising the status of women. The insistence of religious leaders that the practice did not have a religious basis was also important.

Based on the EPLF experience, the government of Eritrea has included information on the negative aspects of female genital mutilation in its health and general education programme. However, it has not made the practice the subject of any special campaign.

SOMALIA

Over 80 per cent of females in Somalia undergo the most radical form of genital mutilation – infibulation. In 1977 when the Somali Women's Democratic Organization (SWDO), the women's wing of the collapsed government of Siad Barre, was formed, Edna Adan Ismail, an experienced health worker, spoke, with government permission, about infibulation. She was afraid that the great hall full of women 'might throw their shoes at me'. Instead they stood up and applauded. So many individuals then wanted to speak that the assembly broke into smaller meetings; at the end each group in turn called for the abolition.

SWDO became the implementing agency appointed by the government for the abolition of female genital mutilation. FGM was carried out in hospitals under general anaesthetic, to eliminate the dangers of damage and infection posed by the traditional operators. The official policy was to encourage pricking of the clitoris to release a drop of blood. This was intended to win support for the eradication of the drastic mutilation of infibulation. Later, FGM was banned in all hospitals; the health education campaign centred on proving that there was no rational reason for mutilation – that it was not healthy, not clean, not Islamic and that it did not even guarantee virginity.

In Khartoum in 1979, at the WHO seminar, two women representing the SWDO, Raqiya Haji Dualeh Abdalla and Mariam Farah Warasme, enumerated the measures they saw as necessary to combat mutilations in Somalia. They felt that legislation was essential, but insufficient. They made a number of points.

1 Any law must be supported by a day-to-day action campaign, throughout the country, in order to inform women and men of medical facts and encourage them to re-examine their attitude.

2 Religious leaders should speak out publicly against infibulation.

3 Discussion groups should be organized among women, workers and young people.

4 Statistical information on irrefutable data gathered by doctors should be collected.

5 The mass media should be widely used to inform the population so that the idea of change can be accepted and a new relationship between the sexes established.

A centre based within the Somalia Academy of Arts and Sciences and funded by the Swedish Agency, SAREC, was set up in the early 1980s to conduct studies on the health, psychological and social aspects of FGM.

North-south cooperation
In 1987 the Somalia Women's Democratic Organization (SWDO), the women's wing of the then ruling party, and the Italian Association for Women and Development, (AIDOS) founded a project with two objectives:

1 to launch and implement a campaign to eradicate infibulation;

2 to strengthen and support SWDO structures in conducting the above campaign.

AIDOS provided technical and methodological support to its Somali counterpart, while SWDO alone was responsible for the content and direction of the campaign. A centre organizing the female anti-mutilation campaign was then set up at SWDO headquarters. In collaboration with ILO-Turin, the project produced five information packs which included audio-visuals for women, young people, religious leaders, medical and paramedical personnel, in the Somali language (which had only been given a script in 1972).

In December 1987, the centre started 'training for trainers' workshops, where participants began to use some of the material produced. It then moved on to seminars for women and was successful in organizing a poetry contest on female genital mutilation. In June 1989, an international conference was organized in Mogadishu, on the theme 'Female Circumcision: Strategies to Bring about Change'. The conference ended with firm resolutions which were intended to provide a framework for ongoing action in Somalia. The Somali Revolutionary Party, the party in power at the time, gave moral support to the project.

However, early in 1991, the Somali Revolutionary Party, having lost control over most of the country, was overthrown. By the end of the year Somalia was in turmoil, torn by clan conflicts and anarchy. The technical base established for the SWDO-AIDOS project was destroyed.

In the present unstable and insecure environment with no functioning government, it is doubtful that anything constructive can be done to eradicate FGM in Somalia. However, millions of Somalis have been forced to flee their homeland. Many are refugees in Western countries. It is this group who stand to gain from a campaign for the eradication of FGM.

SUDAN

The Sudan National Committee on Traditional Practices (SNCTP), the National Chapter of the IAC, is well established with nine full-time staff. It has 109 members in its General Assembly, among them university students, nutritionists, educationalists, social workers, gynaecologists, midwives and health personnel, as well as ten members of the executive board. These are medical practitioners, religious leaders, sociologists and psychologists. It conducts sensitization programmes through seminars, workshops, meetings, group discussions and training and information campaigns. These are targeted at policy-makers, men's and women's organizations, local authority officials, religious and community leaders, university students and government officials. Using educational materials including videos, these sensitization programmes seem to have impressed the participants, who often resolve to pass the message down to the grassroots.

SNTCP undertakes training and information campaigns for local midwives and traditional birth attendants, who are often the perpetrators of FGM. Eradication of harmful traditional practices has been built into the Khartoum Nursing College curriculum.

SNTCP has conducted 'training for trainers' workshops jointly with Maternal Child Health Directorate. The target groups were health workers, community and religious leaders, and local authority officials. It also involves the mass media in disseminating information on harmful traditional practices.

SNTCP received recognition and support from the government, influential individuals and United Nations and voluntary agencies such as UNICEF, the Netherlands Embassy, Radda Barnen, Oxfam Australia, Oxfam UK, Community Aid Africa, Friendship Solidarity Council and Save the Children, UK.

The Babiker Bedri Scientific Assocation for Women's Studies, which is one of the pioneer non-governmental organizations campaigning against FGM in the Sudan, continues with its outreach anti-FGM education programme.

Another organization which was active in the anti-FGM campaign was the Mass Communication Organization for the Eradication of Female Circumcision, which was established in 1987. The UN Family Planning Association (UNFPA) sponsored the group to produce several television programmes on FGM. In 1989, the group was banned by the government.

6

WESTERN COUNTRIES AND PREVENTION

'When I had the operation I was eight years old. I was taken back to Somalia and I had the operation performed. Because I was very young I did not know what was happening to me, what they were doing to me. They strip you. They open your legs apart and they have ladies holding every part of your body, even holding your mouth to prevent you from screaming. I still remember the pain to this day. My sister was circumcised first and straight after she was done I was done. In terms of what has happened to us, we just use the term being 'sewn up', having the clitoris cut off and having been sewn up for us not to have any sexual intercourse or anything! I questioned my mother as to why she did it to me. She said she had to – that it is tradition, it is custom. Anyhow she said she was pressurized into it by grandparents and relatives. And I told her that we were her daughters and we could have died having this operation. The day before I was circumcised, a girl died in the next village and I still remember that. I said to her, you are risking your daughters' lives for the satisfaction of men.

When it is my turn to get married I will have to go to hospital to have the operation undone. I feel whoever I marry, I do not want him to marry me because I am circumcised. For me, I feel my body has been used for somebody else. What is the point of all this except to cause me a lot of pain?' [1]

This testimony was given by a 25-year-old British woman from the Somali community to encourage preventative work on FGM. She was threatened by members of her community for being so candid about her mutilation.

In her testimony, the young woman speaks for the second-generation black girls growing up in the Western world who undergo female genital mutilation. In many ways the protection of black girls growing up in Western countries from the practice is an emergency issue which has not been recognized at policy level. This is not because girls growing up in the Western world are more special than girls, growing up in traditional societies. It is mainly because, unlike their mothers and girls in traditional societies, those girls do not have the same level of psychological conditioning and cultural cushioning to accept female genital mutilation as a normal part of womanhood. The environment in which children grow up is generally more important than their racial heritage, as shown by this personal testimony of an African-German child:

> 'My skin is black. As a result, I'm seen as a foreigner – African or American. I am always asked why my German is so good, where I come from, etc. These questions are irritating. Mostly I answer provocatively that I am German. Even then the questions don't stop – Why, How come, How so? I am African but I am German. My appearance makes me African, my thoughts and my behaviour are German, the way I move is European.' [2]

Second-generation black girls are growing up in a Western environment where the definition of womanhood is not linked to mutilation of the erogenous zones of the female sexual organs. The implications of FGM for the mental health of girls living in the Western world have not been studied. No doubt the response by a child to FGM will depend on several factors – the degree of mutilation, the individual's inner defence mechanisms, consciousness of self and of their rights, parental support, etc. The author has counselled several young women who face physical, psychological and psycho-sexual problems as a direct consequence of FGM, some of whom stressed that they do not feel 'whole', and are not 'proper women'.[3] This, in turn, has had an impact on their self-confidence and their relationships with men. For example, some women have said that, because of lack of sensation, they feel that they are abused each time they have sexual intercourse.

Young women cannot speak out publicly against genital mutilation because of fear of reprisals from other members of the community.[4] They are commonly branded as prostitutes for expressing the mental conflict arising from self, sexuality and FGM.[5] It is important that black women's groups initiating campaigns within their communities against FGM be supported. There are limitations to what they can do however, in instances where issues of parental rights versus children's rights emerge. This is reflected in the following incident.

In 1991, a report was made by a member of the public to a social services department in London, that a Nigerian mother had openly expressed her desire to take her daughter to Nigeria for excision. There was no policy in the social services department at the time on genital mutilation. Social services contacted a Nigerian women's group for them to counsel the mother against excision of the daughter. They were not successful and the mother travelled to Nigeria and the child was excised.[6]

There are other cases like this which the author and her colleagues have faced in the course of counselling communities against FGM. In the USA in September 1994, the author was informed by a community counsellor of the case of an Eritrean father in California who was so concerned that his three-year-old daughter was becoming sexually precocious that he had carried out a clitoridectomy on her himself.[7] There is no law in the USA against FGM, neither has a coherent stance on FGM been integrated into child care policies on child abuse. Such experiences lead the author to believe that in Western countries, the traditional practice of genital mutilation of girls can be classified within existing child care law as a complex form of child physical abuse. Because genital mutilation of girls is a child protection issue, its prevention in the West should not be ghettoized and left to a few women's groups to deal with: it should be brought into mainstream child health and child protection agendas and a concerted effort should be made at all levels to grapple with the problem.

FGM is a very emotive issue in the Western world. People working on the problem have different perspectives on what should be done about it and each perspective has its advantages and disadvantages. This chapter is written from the perspective of the needs of the girl child. Examples are mainly drawn from the UK because an ethnically sensitive approach for the prevention of FGM has been developed there and because it is the only country in the Western world which has been able to integrate FGM into social work practice and has direct practical experience in working on child protection and female genital mutilation. However, this should not be taken as a blueprint for activities in other countries, but rather as a guide to other Western countries which are beginning to develop work in this area. The author acknowledges that the child does not live in a vacuum. The girl child has the right to live with her family and to enjoy the best of the culture of its community, but without fear of being genitally mutilated. The sort of activity which will be discussed is a partnership between the family and the community concerned and professionals in local authority or local government. The needs of adult women who have already been mutilated will also be highlighted.

GENITAL MUTILATION IN THE WESTERN WORLD

Until recently, the focus with regard to female genital mutilation has been on the continent of Africa, where over 80 per cent of female genital mutilation occurs. More recently, it has become apparent that the practice continues, even when people have migrated to societies in which these practices have died out or are little known. Today awareness of this practice in the West is growing, and some action is being taken at governmental level in many Western countries to formulate policies with regard to FGM. It is also heartening to see different community groups organizing round FGM. New organizations are also being set up to give advice and serve as centres of expertise on dealing with the problem. These developments have not happened in a vacuum. They have come about as a result of the hard work and sheer tenacity of black and white feminists, particularly in the

UK and in France, who for more than a decade have worked tire-lessly to raise FGM as a public health and a women and children's human rights issue.

Although the Western media has been blamed for sensational-izing FGM and removing it from its cultural roots, it has made a major contribution to bringing the subject into the open, not only in the West but in the international arena. This in turn is generating interest and support for the work in African countries. However, to increase the in-depth understanding of this practice, the media would need to broaden the scope of their presentation of FGM.

Incidence of FGM in the Western world

Systematic studies on the incidence of FGM in Western countries have not been conducted. Such studies are very difficult as the communities which are likely to practise FGM are marginalized and closed. Also, there are scattered individuals who could live in any part of the country. The practice of FGM within communities which practise it is often a closely guarded secret. Most information currently available on FGM in Western countries is based on rough estimates by women's groups working to combat the practice, using immigration figures and estimates of the extent of the practice in Africa. In 1991, in the UK, an indirect survey was conducted through social services departments. Of 65 local social work departments canvassed, 10 reported casework intervention because of suspected genital mutilation.[8] Whilst experience supports the probability that ethnic groups coming from areas of the world where FGM is widely practised will continue to do so, one cannot assume automatically that all people from these areas are practising FGM. In the UK, the author has worked directly on cases of pending genital mutilation on girls, or with second-generation girls who had already undergone genital mutilation and whose parents were from countries as far apart as Somalia, Sudan, Nigeria, Sierra Leone, Egypt, Malaysia, Ghana and Uganda in a descending order of incidence.

Health care emergencies confirm that FGM is being practised on children in the West. For example, in France in 1982, the three-month-old daughter of Malian parents bled to death as the result of a botched excision performed by a traditional excisor.[9] The dead child's parents were charged with criminal negligence and they were given suspended sentences. In the same year another three-month-old baby was brought to a Paris emergency hospital, bleeding after her Malian father, a migrant worker, had removed her clitoris with a pocket knife.[10] Three other babies have bled to death.[11] In the United Kingdom in 1983, a nurse reported that a Harley Street doctor had performed female genital mutilation on Nigerian visitors to the country.[12] In another case, a young girl from a Birmingham family of Yemeni origin was reported by health workers to have been excised.[13] In Australia in 1993 two girls under two years old were found to be infibulated.[14]

In the last five years there has been an increase of refugees to the West, particularly from countries in the Horn of Africa where the radical form of FGM is widely practised. Within the last three years Canada, for example, has reported an intake of more than 40,000 refugees from Somalia.[15] In Britain the Labour Force Survey (1988) estimated the settled African population in Britain was 122,000, representing an increase of about 30% since 1981.[16] Since 1988, the number of African nationals accepted for settlement in Britain has doubled to around 8,000 per year.[17] The largest proportion of these are refugees from the Horn of Africa. As a result, health care and child welfare systems in the Western world have been faced with a new set of challenges in caring for women who have already undergone genital mutilation, and in protecting girls from undergoing it.

First study conference on genital mutilation of girls in Europe

It is because of the increased concern about genital mutilation of girls in the West that, in 1992, FORWARD (Foundation for Women's Health Research and Development) UK, organized the First Study Conference on Genital Mutilation of Girls in Europe and the Western world. The conference brought together community groups' representatives, community workers and professionals in health and in social work from France, Germany, Italy, the Netherlands, Sweden, the United Kingdom, the USA and the Gambia. The conference was attended by representatives from the following international agencies: the Inter-African Committee (IAC) on Traditional Practices Affecting the Health of Women and Children, WHO, UNICEF, UN Centre for Human Rights, Minority Rights Group, Anti-Slavery International, Defence for Children International, Radda Barnen (Swedish Save the Children), Save the Children, UK. The London Declaration which emerged from the conference energized and empowered the conference participants to promote the campaign for the eradication of genital mutilation of girls in Europe and in the Western world. The recommendations made by the conference were as follows:

1   The conference agreed that any form of genital mutilation of, or genital injury to, the girl child was a violation of her basic human rights, and must be abolished.

2   The conference agreed that the practice of genital mutilation of the girl child had a European-Western dimension requiring a concerted co-ordinated programme of action, using as model the work of FORWARD in the United Kingdom and the groups in France.

3   The conference agreed that combating genital mutilation of the girl child within each country is the primary responsibility of the government.

4   The conference called on all international and national groups within European and other Western countries to pool resources and to co-operate with each other in a coalition against this detrimental practice. To facilitate this, the conference called for the establishment of co-ordination mechanisms, including networking to ensure mutual support and sharing of experiences within a European-Western perspective.

5   The conference called on all groups to take steps at the grassroots level against genital mutilation of the girl child and to ensure the provision of both community support services and rehabilitation programmes as well as their effective delivery. This must include:
(i)   Protection of the child at risk, which must be paramount.

(ii) Education, and promotion of self-help activities within communities practising genital mutilation.

(iii) Rehabilitation of survivors of genital mutilation.

(iv) Training for all health, education and social services professionals working within communities.

6 The conference urged national groups and individuals to promote a legal framework for action, based on specific anti-FGM legislation or laws against injury to the body of the child, including action to ensure that those responsible for the genital mutilation of a girl child are punished.

7 The conference urged all governments and health authorities to stand firm against any attempt to 'medicalize' the genital mutilation of, or genital injury to, the girl child. Further the conference urged all medical and health authorities to develop policies and strategies to eradicate this practice.

8 The conference called on all governments, development assistance agencies, foundations, trusts and all other funding institutions to provide financial support for the European-Western agenda.

9 The conference called for the establishment of a machinery to provide policy and operational guidance for the European-Western programme of action on FGM. The conference accepts the offer of the services of FORWARD in assuming the responsibility for setting up this machinery through FORWARD International, which shall have its own governing body. The activities of FORWARD International shall be:

(i) To promote networking;

(ii) To promote exchange of information and sharing of experiences;

(iii) To assist national groups and individuals, at their request, with community support services, training of professionals and advocacy work;

(iv) Publications.

The conference instructed FORWARD and its affiliates to distribute the Declaration to European-Western governments and to give it the widest possible publicity.

The rest of this chapter is geared towards helping to consolidate policy and practice on the prevention of genital mutilation of girls.

FGM PREVENTION IN THE WESTERN WORLD: POLICY AND PRACTICE

To develop policy one must understand the issues surrounding genital mutilation of girls in the Western world.

The practice

FGM is performed on girls often below the age of twelve. The most vulnerable age in the UK is between five and ten, whereas in France FGM is commonly performed on the under-fives. However, as the campaign in the West deepens, parents are bringing down the age of mutilation. This is mainly because girls in Western countries have alternative information on FGM and there are more support systems for children facing abuse. In the UK, for example, children threatened with parental abuse can call CHILDLINE, a telephone helpline for children.

In the West FGM is obtained by parents in several ways. Parents save money over a long period of time and take girls abroad for the mutilation. Girls commonly are taken to parts of the Middle East, Africa or to the Far East, e.g. Malaysia, for genital mutilation. There are private doctors, midwives and nurses who offer their services to the community on a highly confidential basis. Parents know these professionals, who are often from countries where FGM is practised and are sympathetic to parents' needs. Some professionals may move round the Western countries, offering their services at specific times of the year. There are also traditional excisors known to the communities concerned. They too perform female genital mutilation. In all instances parents and the communities protect the names of both health professionals and excisors.

Migration and preservation of culture

Communities practising FGM in the Western world are largely

settlers, migrants or refugees. It is a well known fact that culture is not static but rather it is changing, adapting and reforming. However, it is generally in the nature of people who have moved to new environments to romanticize about their homeland. It is not uncommon for people to freeze their culture as they remember it in the original homeland, almost as if in a time warp, to the point that even when things have changed in their original country, they will still hang on closely to certain aspects of its culture, particularly rituals which served in the past to bring people together and help to reinforce identity. Rituals of celebration can be very uplifting for both the immigrant community and the host country; for example, the West Indian Carnival in the UK is Europe's largest carnival, bringing joy to hundreds of thousands of British people and visitors to the UK. Equally there are the smaller African music, dance, art and other festivals which have become a feature of most capitals of the world. However, there are also negative rituals and practices such as genital mutilation of girls, which can be confused with positive rituals of culture which would be maintained by immigrant communities.

FGM has a compulsive, habitual aspect to it which has hardly been examined. This is explored in the following example.

In a documentary about FGM entitled *Scarred for Life* produced by ABC News (Day One Show) and shown on American television in 1993, a Somali couple were interviewed about whether they intended to have their two daughters genitally mutilated. Both were university graduates. The husband did not want his daughters to be mutilated but the wife did. She herself had undergone infibulation as a child. She explained that she would not put them through infibulation but would have clitoridectomy performed on the girls, in a hospital, under anaesthetic and in a hygienic environment. Her two main reasons for wanting clitoridectomy performed on her daughters were that she was concerned about their future marriageability and was also worried that they would be different.

The second reason the mother gave – 'they would be different' – is what I would like to focus on. What she meant was that her daughters would be different from her and from other women in the community. In other words, the female who has not undergone genital mutilation is an aberration. This is a psychological issue which can be dealt with through counselling, encouragement and support. Men may need counselling to re-adjust themselves to viewing the unmutilated women as normal. However, if this counselling is not offered or accepted, there is likelihood that a mother will go ahead and put her daughters through clitoridectomy even though she may not be under direct pressure to do so, as would have been the case in Africa, and even if aware of specific health problems that the child can face in later life. There was no child care policy on FGM in Atlanta, Georgia, where the couple featured in the documentary were living. No one knows what happened to the two girls.

The unmet needs of black girls in marginalized communities

Because of limited understanding of the practice, FGM in the West is trapped in a cultural ghetto, it is not viewed as an abusive practice, consequently the subject has not received the attention it deserves from child protection agencies. As a result it seems to some that the life of the black female child is of less value than that of other children. Indeed specialized children's agencies focusing on child protection have only responded to this issue after much pressure from women's groups. The end result is that the black female child's needs are not being fully met in these developed countries.

Gender oppression within minority communities

The fact that female genital mutilation is about gender oppression has already been explained (see Chapter 3). Gender oppression is something which can become further entrenched within disadvantaged minority communities in the Western world. Because of racism faced by minority communities, there is often pressure on community members not to disclose the dirty linen of the community to the wider public. FGM is viewed by the community as something private and cultural. Media exposures of the physical horrors of FGM can be interpreted by community members as a calculated attack on the culture and the community, and this may be exploited by some community activists and male chauvinists in the community. People viewed as collaborators in such media exposures are intimidated. This has the direct effect of silencing ordinary women and men in the community who may want to speak out against FGM or other forms of gender oppression.

FGM can also become entrenched in Western countries because white liberal culture is often viewed as decadent by chauvinist men, fundamentalist religious leaders and cultural nationalists within communities practising FGM. As a result, rituals and practices which reinforce virginity, chastity and fidelity assume greater importance. In the author's experience, infibulation and excision is a power issue within the family and in the community and is often inflicted on young girls in the community as a form of social control to prevent young women from marrying outside their ethnic group. It can also be used to control what families may classify as unacceptable behaviour. For example, the author has come across several instances of chauvinist men and parents expressing fears about girls masturbating, young women becoming lesbians, or girls engaging in sexual intercourse and losing their virginity and becoming 'loose' like women from the decadent culture.

Racism

The historical and social context of female genital mutilation is barely understood in western countries. Very few white people know that clitoridectomy is not exclusive to black cultures but has been performed on white women in the past – not as a precondition for marriage but as 'treatment' for misbehaviour. Except in gender studies and in feminist circles, such information is generally hidden. FGM is seen by the mainstream white population as something totally alien to white culture. Knowledge that FGM is practised by some black people on girls provokes racist remarks or paternalism towards the people who practise it. Many black people have confused FGM as gender oppression with the rich African culture, and because they look to their African heritage with pride, racist remarks on FGM can evoke strong sentiments of cultural nationalism. Racist remarks have the effect of putting many black people on the defensive about FGM. Racist remarks also trigger guilt feelings in liberal whites who may mean well but confuse the whole issue by condoning FGM within a naive concept of multi-culturalism. Specifically, African women campaigning against FGM in the West have the triple burden of having to confront gender oppression, white liberal guilt and racism within the community.

The prevention of genital mutilation of girls in the Western world gets caught up in a web of adult politics of culture, class, gender and race. People who are keen to do something are often paralysed into inaction. To work in this area is to expose oneself to various levels of political criticism, as outlined above. To avoid confronting the pain of criticism, many policy-makers, professionals, funders and women leaders rationalize that it is better to leave the solution to women within the community and argue that FGM is too sensitive an issue for them to deal with. As has been already explained, however, in most cases those particular women are powerless to confront FGM alone.

CHARTING THE PATH TO PREVENTION OF FGM IN THE WESTERN WORLD

Working within a legislative framework

There is a belief by many people that once a law is passed against female genital mutilation then that is the end of the matter. This is not so. A law is only one component of the solution to the problem. Genital mutilation is performed on children and, as with other forms of child abuse, children are too young to understand or to resist. To get a case into the courts there have to be complaints to the police. Children are unlikely to be able to make them. As the practice is condoned as tradition by adults in the family and in the community at large, one would not expect adults to go to the police. Private doctors and excisors who perform these mutilations do it on a clandestine basis, so the chances of finding out that FGM has occurred are limited to emergency situations, for example, when children have died or a child is admitted to a casualty department bleeding or with infections, as has happened in France. Even at this stage many doctors and nurses may not report this to the police or child protection agencies.

A law does provide a clear indication that FGM performed on children is not acceptable in a country. This in itself can be a major educational tool. It also means that families who do not want to practise FGM on their girls can invoke the law to back up their position. Recently, a group of second-generation black young women in the UK asked the author about the possibility of suing their local authorities for not taking action to protect them from genital mutilation when they were young. That was an interesting idea but nothing much could be done, for at the time that these girls were mutilated there were no laws against FGM, nor any awareness that it was a human rights abuse.

Another problem is that many parents may take the girls to other countries where FGM is not illegal and get these mutilations performed. When this happens, the laws of the country in which the person resides are irrelevant. The law might be able to stop a child being taken to another country for FGM to be performed (as in the UK), but Sweden is the only country which has a law making adults liable for prosecution if girls resident in Sweden are taken and mutilated in countries where there are laws against FGM. The loophole in the law which allows adults to move freely around countries to get mutilation performed on their girls can be closed if all countries in the world take steps to initiate laws against genital mutilation of girls. This may be quite difficult in the foreseeable future, but it should be possible to achieve this, for example, within the European Community.

The law makes it possible to work on FGM as an abuse within the framework of child care law. In an emergency, where children are found to be at risk of undergoing FGM, steps could be taken to protect them. In this context the law is used in a preventative way. There is much lethargy and confusion amongst professionals in the Western world in working to eradicate FGM. It is the law which guides them in their work. Nurses assisting doctors in such mutilations can invoke the law and refuse to co-operate. They can also report such cases to their professional disciplinary bodies.

FGM is a complex form of abuse which needs to be addressed

within the framework of child protection but with a preventative focus. It should be introduced onto the widest possible agendas in health promotion for the community directly concerned and society in general. It is only by attacking the problem on all fronts simultaneously that the practice can be eradicated rather than being driven further underground.

Professional queries answered

Several questions are asked daily by involved policy-makers, agencies, community workers and individuals as to how FGM prevention could operate within a child protection system. The most common are answered here.

(a) *Where should one place genital mutilation of girls?*
Because of the complexity of FGM, and the need for inter-agency co-operation in this area, one agency will have to take the responsibility and to co-ordinate activities for its prevention. Because FGM is first and foremost a child protection issue and the leading agencies in the child protection field in Western countries are social services departments, they should take up responsibility for co-ordination of activity on FGM within a given area.

(b) *How do you know which groups practise FGM and in which areas would you find them?*
FGM is practised by people originating from areas in the world where the practice is widespread. You can be sure that if it is practised by settler, immigrant and refugee communities in other Western countries it will be a miracle if such communities in your area are totally free from the practice. The quickest way to confirm this is to gather data by employing field workers who know the communities.

(c) *Is female genital mutilation a category of abuse?*
The following are the classifications of child abuse in social work in the UK. However, the author has found that there are similarities between the UK definition of abuse and those in France and

in the United States.

1   *Physical injury*: actual or likely physical injury to a child, or failure to prevent physical suffering to a child, including deliberate poisoning, suffocation and Munchhausen's Syndrome by proxy.

2   *Neglect*: persistent or severe neglect of a child or failure to protect a child from exposure to any kind of danger, including cold or starvation, or extreme failure to carry out important aspects of care, resulting in significant impairment to the child's health or development, including non-organic failure to thrive.

3   *Sexual Abuse*: actual or likely sexual exploitation of a child or adolescent by an adult for his or her sexual gratification.

4   *Emotional Abuse*: actual or likely severe adverse effects on the emotional and behaviourial development of a child caused by persistent or severe emotional ill-treatment or rejection. All abuse involves some emotional mistreatment.

Under the above category of abuse FGM can be placed under physical injury. It is important to remember that community members will find it difficult to see FGM initially as a form of child abuse. They will stress that other forms of abuse are calculated and intentional but FGM is not. FGM is community approved and is performed by loving parents as an act of love – to make their daughters marriageable and acceptable in their community. This position should be acknowledged but the reality is that at the end of the day the child suffers serious and irreparable physical injury.

One can see similarities between FGM and other forms of abuse, e.g.; beating children to inculcate good behaviour and to discipline them. In Western culture, this used to be widely accepted as normal practice. An old English adage asserts 'Spare the rod and spoil the child'. This was preached from pulpits and was a practice condoned by the wider society. Parents who beat their children to inculcate discipline would also say they love their children. Beating children and injuring them is classified as child abuse. If a child is found with bruises all over his body this will be investigated. So if the child's sexual organs are removed or damaged with the aim of suppressing the normal functioning of this organ, should not this also be the subject of investigation?

FGM can be classified as a pseudo-religious practice for it is based on strong belief systems. Although parents have a fundamental right to raise and educate their children as they choose, Western courts in several instances have had to intervene when the belief systems of parents endanger the well-being of children.[18] An example is Jehovah's Witness parents refusing blood transfusions for very sick children, or faith healers refusing medical treatment for their children.

(d) *How does one approach this form of abuse?*
One should approach the issue with great sensitivity. One might decide on a preventative focus and work with families. One might develop guidelines and procedures to address this abuse. The key issue is that policy needs to be developed on FGM, and those who develop policy must be clear that FGM is gender oppression and child abuse.

A child protection system on FGM

The first step towards developing a system for prevention would be to look at community responses to viewing FGM as an abuse. If a community has a deep-seated belief that the unmutilated woman is an aberration, unacceptable, unfit for marriage and for society; that she is dirty and a prostitute, that she is impure, she cannot pray and men will not enjoy sex with her if she is not 'sewn shut'; if, when FGM is performed it is done within the context of coming-of-age celebrations and if women in ethnic groups who do not practise excision are viewed as not 'proper' women then there will be outrage when FGM is classified as an abuse.

The initial response will be anger, then denial and fear. It would be a traumatic process for many women and community members to re-evaluate the whole practice. However, if women and communities are not supported to come through this pain and face the reality of the seriousness of the damage done to the child, the lies and the denial which have sustained FGM for centuries will continue and the cycle of abuse will not be broken. This is not the first time that policy-makers and professionals would face anger from families and the public on the issue of child abuse. The process of change is similar to the response of the Western public to all forms of child abuse. The facts of child physical abuse and child sexual abuse were denied and resisted when they were first brought into the open. Eventually these abuses were acknowledged. The same process is occurring in relation to the traditional abuse of female genital mutilation.

What the author is trying to stress here is that initially there will be an angry response from many community members for taking action to protect the black female child from FGM but this should not be used as an excuse to ignore the issue. What is required is space for this anger to be expressed and support for families and communities who have to acknowledge that FGM is a very bad thing to happen to a child in the first place.

The following case history from a London social services department underlines the need to provide space for people to handle the upheavals which they are bound to go through before change comes about.

'In 1991 Inderjit Wilkhu, an Ealing social worker, was allocated a family where it was feared two girls under the age of ten would be circumcised. An older sibling had already been circumcised, and following a case conference the two younger ones were placed on the "at risk" register.

Then, Wilkhu knew little about the practice. She turned to FOR-WARD for guidance and decided on a holistic, persuasive approach.

The family were political refugees and had no concept of UK child protection work: 'I had to explain why we were involved, the legal requirements and the context,' she says. 'In my first session I said: "I am here because it is against the children's welfare. It is not considered a proper practice in this country. I am not against you. I want to work with you." Of course they were very angry. But I said if you think this is good for your children then convince me so I can do it for my children. In this way I opened up the debate.'

Wilkhu argues that you cannot tackle the issue without appreci-

ating the family's position: 'As refugees they are disadvantaged. They may be turned back any minute. Family members may have been killed, all this put them in a weak position.' The family was an open and loving one, and Wilkhu was careful to balance her intervention by emphasizing the positive aspects of the family's culture. In a session on women's virginity she talked about how it was important in Asian cultures too. "But Asian women don't have to be infibulated."

All the sessions were planned, and eventually she established a rapport. "Two-thirds of the way through I noticed they were changing. It was a softly, softly approach but I was always assertive about how wrong circumcision was."

While she worked with the family. Wilkhu knew that infibulation could still take place: "I was never 101 per cent sure that it wouldn't. I was most concerned about the summer holiday period when they could have had it done without it being noticed."

The mother made it clear that the circumcision would take place if she considered it in her daughters' best interests. She was prepared to go to court if anyone tried to stop her. Similarly, Wilkhu held the threat of wardship proceedings as a last resort.

The work was successful...Wilkhu argues that people working with female genital mutilation should be chosen for their ability to empathize and respect other cultures. She says it might have taken a white worker longer to gain the family's confidence: "initially they might have been seen as threatening".

All professionals working in areas where communities are known to carry out the practice should be aware of the facts, she says. "But it should be of interest to all free thinking people." [19]

The diagram overleaf shows how a child protection system for female genital mutilation should work.

TABLE 3

How a child protection system for female genital mutilation should work

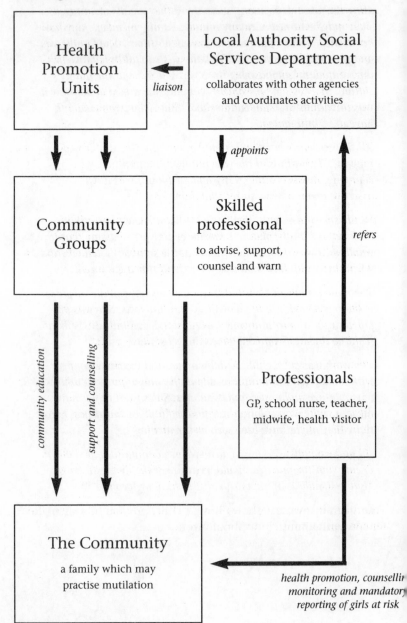

SOURCE: Updated from *Child Protection and Female Genital Mutilation* by Rodney Hedley and Efua Dorkenoo

A system for preventing girls undergoing FGM will only work if it is given the same recognition as other forms of child abuse, if procedures and guidelines are built to support professionals working on FGM, resources allocated to promote this work and activities co-ordinated properly.[20]

Long-term preventative measures

Long-term preventative action on FGM will involve supporting communities to address the issue through health promotion and furthering this work through those agencies – health, social services and education – which are directly in touch with families and children and could provide education or be in a position to monitor and to protect children at risk of FGM.

The education programme should start during the ante-natal period. Midwives should receive training on FGM so that they can provide good clinical care to infibulated women and be able to counsel women and their partners on FGM. The midwife should be trained to be aware of at-risk groups. During ante-natal visits the midwife should ask the pregnant woman whether she has undergone female genital mutilation. This will facilitate better service provision as, in many cases in the West, midwives do not know that a woman is infibulated and are therefore not able to offer appropriate care and delivery. After delivery the midwife should inform the health visitor who takes over the care of the baby for the following five years. If a mother has undergone genital mutilation and has delivered a girl there might be a possibility that FGM will occur in the future. She can follow up with health education for the mother over the five-year period when the girl is brought for immunization, developmental check-ups, etc. It is part of her general brief to be alert to any form of child abuse. For example, if she discovered bruises or burns on a child she would investigate further, and if she is concerned that a child is being abused she will report this to the social services who have a mandate to deal with child abuse. She will be able to incorporate monitoring the child for FGM into her work.

The following is an example of a case in which the author was involved in Bristol, UK, which highlights this point.

> *'On one of her follow-up home visits to see how an 18-month-old girl was faring (mother had missed some past appointments for the baby clinic), a Malaysian mother informed the health visitor she would be travelling abroad for the little girl to be circumcised in Malaysia. The health visitor tried to counsel the mother out of this but it did not work. Social services became involved and together with the author and a counsellor from the Malaysian community, they were able to persuade the mother not to make the child undergo circumcision.'*[21]

The father of the child was English and he was ambivalent about the practice. The process of changing the mind of the mother was not easy. The whole case had to go through the family courts. With counselling the mother went to Malaysia and came back without mutilating her daughter. As I have pointed out before, families need space to re-evaluate the whole practice. This will be projected as an intense emotional expression. Ordinarily, professionals tend to back down when such intense emotions are expressed but it is the very time that we need to stay put and to support families to deal with their pain at letting go of redundant practice.

After the age of five the child is at school. Primary school age is one of the periods where little girls are most 'at risk' of female genital mutilation. In most countries in the Western world which provide a free national health care system there are school nurses, community paediatricians and educational social workers attached to schools. They, too, could have a role in health promotion and in child protection. Another case in which the author was involved in a London borough illustrates this role.

> *'At the end of the school year, the school paediatrician was making her normal health checks with all the children in the primary school. During this period she will do hearing checks, eye tests and discuss with parents any problems in terms of the development of the child. In the course of one of these discussions, a Somali refugee mother openly requested genital mutilation for her two girls who were six and eight years old. As soon as she mentioned the word "circumcision" the six-year-old started to protest.'*[22]

The doctor informed her that FGM was against the law in the country and explained the health implications to the mother. It was just before the summer holidays and she was concerned that if there was no follow-up the girls might be mutilated. Counselling families against genital mutilation requires time and patience. The case was reported to the social services department and the children placed on the 'at-risk' register for cases of threatened child abuse. A social worker was attached to the family. In conjunction with the author and a counsellor from the Somali community, they were able to provide the necessary information and to support the family through the process of not mutilating the girls. The girls were not removed from their families but social services' intervention acted as a major deterrent for the parents making the girls undergo FGM. It gave time to work intensively with the family.

This work was not easy. The husband was furious that his children were on the 'at-risk' register. He was very well educated and felt it was against his 'honour'. He had a right of access to a lawyer who participated in subsequent case conferences. However, the children were protected in the end without disruption to the family unit. The father's 'honour' was bruised and social services took a lot of criticism for this intervention. Some of the members of the Somali community complained that the intervention by social services was racist, but the key point is that in the end the children were protected from female genital mutilation. Monitoring continues after the children are removed from the 'at-risk' register through school and through the family health practitioner.

Primary school teachers need to be aware of female genital mutilation as they, too, have a professional responsibility to act in cases of child abuse. The following case, again in a London borough, illustrates this role.

'Just before the summer holiday in 1994, a six year old girl whose mother was a Somali refugee, in a general discussion on what all the children were going to do over the summer holidays, said that she was going to Kenya with her mother and she was going to have an injection into her vagina. The teacher was con-

*cerned that it could be genital mutilation. She went through the
procedures laid down within the school on reporting child abuse.
The case went to social services department and a social worker
was allocated the case.*[23]

The mother initially denied that she had the intention of making
her daughter undergo female genital mutilation. However, on
subsequent investigation it transpired that the older daughter had
undergone infibulation. Her own mother was sick in hospital in
Kenya and she planned to visit her and have the two younger
girls – aged eight and six – undergo genital mutilation. It was like
killing two birds with one stone. She was aware of the law but she
said this was a religious requirement. In the case conference she
was upset and very angry. She pointed out the suffering she and
her children had gone through escaping the war in Somalia and
coming to Britain. She thought she could have peace of mind
once she was in Britain but here she was being harassed by social
workers because she wanted to circumcise her girls which was a
Somali tradition and a religious obligation.

All the professionals on the case conference (social workers,
the children's teacher, police child protection officers, black
women's organization representatives, translator, general practitioner, school nurse) were deeply moved. What were they to do?
It is often at this point that most people get paralyzed into inaction. Communities practising FGM know about the weakness of
Western policy makers and professionals and they use this to
their maximum advantage. Everybody at the case conference
could empathize with the mother's situation; at the same time
they had to think about the needs of the children as a priority.
The law was clear that FGM was a criminal offence and under
the UK Children Act local authorities have responsibility to protect a girl found at risk of genital mutilation, so the professionals
were empowered to be firm on the issue.

This case was very interesting as the crisis situation ended up
as something positive for the family. Social services sponsored
the mother to go and visit her sick mother in Kenya. Meanwhile
the mother agreed to leave the children temporarily in the care
of social services whilst she travelled. The housing situation for

the family was not so good (e.g.; there were safety concerns, such as broken glass doors) and social services improved it. In addition, the older daughter, who was already infibulated, was not adjusting well to school and was very withdrawn. She was very angry that her younger sister had let out what she considered a family secret on female genital mutilation. She was insistent that all of her sisters ought to be genitally mutilated. Extra English lessons were arranged for her and a child psychologist was recommended to support her. Everybody did their best to help the mother to readjust to the new environment but it was made clear to her that mutilating the children was unacceptable. A Somali social worker was attached to the family to work with her to overcome her pain at letting go of this practice.

Child protection interventions are not always successful, but at least some children may be spared from genital mutilation. Every little girl is special and each one saved from genital mutilation is a major achievement. This work cannot be done without a clear-cut law against FGM and directives which give professionals a mandate to act to protect girls. The other thing that the reader must have noticed is that work on FGM demands inter-agency co-operation.

This is sensitive area of work. It is natural that communities will fight to keep FGM off the child protection agenda. Many are afraid that community members will be criminalized and their children taken away from them, but as the case studies presented show, the focus of child protection is preventive and the law is used as a last resort. FGM can be handled sensitively by agencies directly concerned with the welfare of children if there is policy on it.

Developing policy on FGM

What should be incorporated in a child protection policy on FGM? This may differ from one social services department to the other. Such a policy might incorporate the following:[24]
1   Clarification of the definition of FGM. For example it would need to clarify whether sticking needles into the clitoris for ritualistic purposes, removing the hood of the clitoris, or

removing the tip of the clitoris should be classified as FGM. It should specify the people in the community likely to be affected.

2   There should be an acknowledgement that there is a deep-rooted belief and value system surrounding FGM and normally the people who practise it see it as beneficial. For this reason responses to FGM need to be sensitively handled and care must be taken to guard against aggressive interventions.

3   There should be recognition and acknowledgement of the cultural and traditional practices of a multi-racial communities, but the policy should state that it is against genital mutilation of girls in all its forms. The relevant law should be spelt out.

4   Definition of genital mutilation as *child physical abuse* should be spelt out.

5   Direction of the campaign should be made clear, e.g. discouraging genital mutilation of girls primarily through an educational programme, with the participation of the Departments of Health, Social Services, Education and by voluntary groups.

6   There should be clear directives on what agencies should do if aware or informed that a girl has been or may be subjected to female genital mutilation. For example, a Child Protection Investigation may be set in motion. This will have its own procedures.

7   The policy should spell out what needs to be done with a girl in danger of genital mutilation, for example she might be placed on the Child Protection Register under the category of Physical Abuse.

8   It will spell out what will happen to the girl who has been genitally mutilated, for example, she will not be placed on the register of child abuse but might be offered counselling and medical help if necessary, and a plan of action developed to work with the family if there are younger girl siblings in the family who may be in danger of mutilation.

9   The emphasis of work in cases of actual or threatened genital mutilation should be clarified, for example, this will be through education and persuasion.

10 Certain aspects of child care law which can be invoked should be clarified, e.g.; under the UK Children Act legal proceedings could include a Prohibitive Steps Order (UK Children Act, Section 8) which can be made to prevent parents carrying out a particular act without the consent of the Court (e.g. removing the child from the UK so that mutilation can be carried out abroad.) A Care Supervision Order (UK Children Act, Section 31 (1))may be needed. Removal from home should be considered only as a last resort.

11 Directions on the role of the police with regard to FGM. For example, in the UK there are Police Child Protection Officers who are part of inter-agency child protection teams. In cases of Child Protection Investigations on FGM they should be invited to participate.

Generally, in child protection interventions, the police child protection officers will work in a collaborative way with social workers, often leaving social services to undertake education and counselling on threatened genital mutilation. However, should a girl be found bleeding from a fresh genital mutilation, or dead from a botched genital mutilation as has happened in France, then it is up to the police to take action as specified under the laws of the country. Criminal prosecutions are unpleasant but a reality. The author believes that if a preventative system is put into place, then criminal prosecutions may not occur or will be reduced to a minimum.

The real test of a policy is whether it is implemented or whether it remains on paper gathering dust.

Implementation of policy

Training of professionals in various fields is a must in a preventative programme. Knowledge of FGM evokes various responses in professionals: many are scared of the subject. In many instances, when professionals are being trained to deal with FGM, some, even health professionals, have actually fainted or felt sick. They need support to overcome their fear of the subject before they do any work on it. In other instances, knowledge that girls are being mutilated evokes anger, hurt and pain. It also evokes racist feelings. These negative feelings could turn into scapegoating and blaming of minority communities. The feelings can only be overcome through training, to strengthen professionals' skills so that they are able to work with families and the community in an anti-racist way.

Advice for professionals

Inderjeet Wilkhu, a senior black social worker in London, with experience of working with families to protect children from FGM, offers the following advice. Child protection social workers, health professionals, school teachers and community workers need to be aware of where people from the ethnic minority who practise FGM live and to be aware of this practice. In other words they need to be vigilant.

1 Watch out for long holidays, trips abroad, long periods of sickness and for children's playground talk about adults' plans for them to be purified.
2 If suspicious refer this child to Child Protection Services.
3 Child Protection Services will have to investigate, collect the background information, family history, other factual details, etc.
4 Interview the parents and explain your concern that a child may be at risk of FGM. Is it true? How do they feel about it? If they express their intention to have their children done, ask for their reasons; social, cultural, religious, traditional, other.
   If they deny intending to put their daughters through FGM, do not believe them immediately as they may be responding by telling you what you want to hear. Ask how they have reached this decision. An enlightened parent will share her experiences, view them as negative and would prefer her children not to suffer pain. By intervening, you are giving the parents permission to validate their own feelings and they will not act under any familial or societal pressure.
5 There should be ongoing assessments through regular visits to the family.

6   Information should be shared with multi-disciplinary teams – to monitor the children's health and progress through schools, health visitors, etc.

7   It is important to explain to the parents your statutory responsibilities and the legal framework under which you are working. If necessary this can be done again and again as it might not sink in at once.

8   Tell them what legal powers you have to protect children, which might mean compulsorily removing the children from their care without their co-operation.

9   Encourage them to speak about their distress and conflicts over this matter, and let them know that to co-operate with you is the best way to safeguard their children's interests and promote their welfare.

10 Praise them for co-operating, acknowledge the positive aspects of their parenting.

11 Use interpreters who are proven supporters of the abolition of FGM rather than those who may have a vested interest in continuing the practice.

12 Review at regular intervals and hold multi-disciplinary meetings to share information on the family's view points over this matter to find what stage they are at and whether they are moving towards the desired direction of changing their minds about genitally mutilating their daughter.

CAMPAIGNING GROUPS ON FGM

There are different groups campaigning against FGM. Some are mixed black and white groups. Others are purely black. Some are all female, others are mixed male and female. Some are health pressure groups and others are grassroots community educational groups. The pressure groups often break the ice on FGM, bringing it from the private into the open and opening up avenues for small community groups to operate. Their work tends to be catalytic, focusing on getting FGM on to different mainstream agendas of child protection and health promotion. Some groups specialize in training, developing educational materials, supporting the development of grassroots projects and acting as advisory back-up for professionals in evolving policies and in making child protection interventions. Other groups take a low profile approach, working quietly within the community informing women and families and counselling them against FGM. These latter groups highlight the dangers of racism and put brakes on anyone wanting to address FGM in an insensitive manner. All groups are complementary in the anti-FGM campaign and their work needs to be supported.

ADDRESSING THE HEALTH NEEDS OF EXCISED/INFIBULATED WOMEN

Excised and infibulated women have specialized needs which have been ignored or dealt with on a trial and error basis. In Western countries severe forms of female genital mutilation present challenges to midwives and obstetricians in providing proper ante- and post-natal care. For example, professionals need training to know how to deliver infibulated women. The provision of health care for women or girls who have been genitally mutilated should be appropriate and sensitive to their needs. Health promotion work through women's health services can develop appropriate information and health promotion materials and actively contribute to outreach work and raising awareness.

Health professionals will also need to be fully conversant with the ethical and legal implications of FGM, and the emotions and sensitivity which surround the subject. In the UK, health visitors have a duty under the UK Central Council for Nursing (UKCC) Professional Code of Conduct to participate in child protection issues. However, they will need to keep in close contact with social workers who have responsibility in child protection. Health workers will need guidelines on specific aspects of clinical care of women who have undergone infibulation. For example, they will need guidance on the issue of restitching after childbirth and special measures should be adopted by medical staff to provide a standard of care which respects the dignity and right to privacy of women and girls and also offers support and continuity of care. The use of trained interpreters is critical to providing such standards of care since many first generation immigrants do not speak English or other European languages.

The professional bodies for nurses, midwives and doctors should prompt action on FGM by issuing guidance to their members. An example is the excellent comprehensive guidance produced by the Royal College of Nursing in the UK, the world's largest professional union of nurses.[25]

A comprehensive health service can only be offered in countries where there is a national free health care policy, e.g. the UK, Canada and Sweden. In countries like the USA, where health care is privatized, such services will not reach out to marginal communities. Gaining access to health services in countries with a privatized health service involves taking out health insurance policies which are out of reach of the poor, including immigrant population groups. Poor women may not have any ante-natal care, neither will there be full school nursing or health visiting services for children from poor communities. Community outreach through women's groups and through social workers will be the main avenue for preventative work.

Midwives'/obstetricians' guide to management of infibulated women during pregnancy and delivery

Infibulation almost seals a woman up. During marriage the opening left for urination and the passage of menstrual blood needs to be widened. In Western countries women may have difficulties in accessing health care service for de-infibulation (opening up). As a result they may end up getting pregnant with still a very tiny opening (the husband's sperm seeps through). The scar tissue presents a barrier for delivery.

Many women are very conscious that Western health professionals are not familiar with caring for infibulated women. They may have heard stories from other women of being made to feel like freaks when they attend for ante-natals. Because of this, and coupled with language barriers, some women may not attend ante-natals and may just present themselves in labour.

When women present in labour the midwife or obstetrician will have difficulty performing vaginal examination to assess the progress of the labour. Emphasis may instead be placed on observation of external signs such as anal dilatation, or on more subtle signs such as the ring in the uterine muscle (distinct from Bandl's ring) visible during contractions above the symphysis pubis which is described in Russian midwifery text books.[26,27] Rectal examination may be used to assess cervical dilation.[28]

Application of scalp electrodes, insertion of intra-uterine pressure catheters or performing fetal blood sampling may be impossible.[29] An inability to provide adequate fetal monitoring may force the obstetrician to perform a Caesarean section.[30] Even at this stage urinary catheterization might be impossible.[31]

The following is service delivery developed at Northwick Park hospital, London to enhance the ante-natal care of infibulated women:

1   An African midwife and an obstetrician see women throughout their pregnancy. The advantage is that there is continuity of care and women see the same professionals at all the visits. This provides room for building a patient-client relationship of support and a trust critical for counselling and sensitive care.
2   There is an interpreting service so that language barriers can be overcome.
3   Women are offered the choice of de-infibulation in the second trimester of pregnancy if they so wish.

Procedure for de-infibulation

Dr Mary McCaffrey, an obstetrician/gynaecologist who runs the African Well-Women Clinic, has put forward the following suggestions based on her experience of working with women.

1   Clients should be counselled. For example, they should be aware that passing urine after de-infibulation might be different. If this is not done they may interpret the difference as being incontinent.
2   For many patients the sensation of touch triggers 'flashbacks' of the infibulation procedure in childhood. The use of local anaesthesia or epidural anaesthesia may not be appropriate.
3   The patient is placed in lithotomy. The perineum is painted with either Chlorhexidine or Betadine solution.
4   The anterior flap of skin is lifted with a dissecting forceps and

incised with a scalpel or surgical scissors. Where possible the clitoris is exposed (see p.11: Extended infibulated vulva).

5 The raw edges on either side are oversewn with an absorbable suture material such as 3/0 catgut or Dexon.

6 Adequate post-operative analgesia is vital. If patients are allowed to suffer pain this may further reinforce negative ideas about de-infibulation and discourage other women from having the procedure performed.

7 Following discharge from hospital, patients are advised to have daily baths.

Patients and their partners should be counselled during the ante-natal period on re-infibulation and its health conse-quences. Often, when time is given for psychosexual coun-selling, clients do not request re-infibulation. It is necessary for the law and professional bodies to provide legal and ethi-cal guidelines on re-infibulation.

EDUCATION WORK WITH CHILDREN THROUGH SCHOOLS

Children are the parents of tomorrow. Teachers, school nurses, school doctors and health education advisors have a key role to play in health promotion and child protection. The schools are the best place to both educate and support children. Children who are already excised and infibulated need extra support. They may take a long time urinating or be off school with menstrual problems and so on. The schools have also provided avenues for children to seek protection for themselves or for their younger siblings. The drawback in doing education work through schools is that often black children face racial abuse as a matter of course and there is a need for caution in dealing with their education needs so as to avoid the targeting of black girls by other children for racial abuse.

Janice Lee, an experienced teacher working in Cardiff in Wales, got over this problem by setting up, as part of English classes, a programme of social education for refugee and immi-grant children between the ages of 13 and 15 years. This has not only proved useful for discussing cultural differences, but also as

155

a means for discussing deeply felt emotions relating to events in their lives. Once, the subject of FGM was broached, by asking, among other things, what had been their most terrifying experience. Once Janice indicated that she knew about FGM, the girls were able, often for the first time, to openly discuss the issue. At this stage Janice took great care not to be judgemental but rather led the discussion gently to a consideration of what they felt should be happening today. Often the girls have never considered the probability of changes and they need to take the idea on board.

Parental consent might be needed for such activities. This is a tricky area and it is possible that consent might be withheld. In such situations there is need to develop other strategies to address children's needs. For example, the author has had discussions with young women who have undergone genital mutilation and have already gone through the schooling system in Western countries. They suggest that children as young as six could be called to meet with teachers and school nurses privately and be informed on the subject. If FGM is incorporated in Child Abuse Laws and there is a policy in a given area on FGM, with the participation of responsible community members, it will be a backbone of support for professionals in schools. Teachers, school nurses or educational social workers, together with responsible community members, will devise a strategy to discuss FGM with parents and for parents to be informed of professional responsibilities with regard to child abuse.

Materials used for teaching about FGM must be carefully chosen to avoid traumatizing children. A case in point, is that of an artist who walked into FORWARD'S office to show off a model of infibulation which she had made with pig's liver. A teenager who was in the office at the time and who had undergone FGM became hysterical. This artist had planned to sell the models to schools.

Islington and Camden Health Authority in London, for example, recommends that appropriate mechanisms be developed to ensure that:

1   girls have access to information or advice anonymously, if they so wish;

2 confidentiality is assured in respect of personal advice or support;
3 young girls or young women who have experienced FGM
   have access to peer support, if they wish;
4 educational staff should have access to training on FGM.

GRASSROOTS ANTI-FGM PROJECTS IN COMMUNITY EDUCATION

Community education is a major cornerstone for change. The
work of professionals will be much easier when communities are
empowered to raise the issue of FGM themselves. Local authorities should work in partnership with the communities to open
up spaces within the community for such activities. Health
authorities and local authorities should be aware of community
perceptions and concerns and should work strategically, supporting the active involvement of those directly concerned. Care
must be taken over how resources are distributed for community
education. The experience gained in the UK is that different
groups practice FGM, and that community groups may not necessarily be interested in FGM prevention. Issues of migration,
housing, racial harassment or promoting cultural activities tend
to be a priority for many such groups. Giving funding to one
group does not guarantee that the project will reach out to
everybody. Africans are not homogeneous. There are divisions
within groups, such as the Somalis, who are socially organized
into different clans which are often in conflict with one another.
An Issaq clan group may not be able to work with a Darood clan
group, and so on.
   To reach out to all people in need of services, it is sometimes
best in terms of quality and cost-effectiveness to develop an FGM
project outside the established groups and direct the service to
all the groups. For example, the Refugee Council in Gothenburg,
Sweden, runs a community education outreach programme on
FGM which is funded by the Ministry of Health and Social
Affairs. The Refugee Council employed a Somali worker, who was
able to get leaders of the different clans to come together to form
a working group on FGM through a process of negotiation. The

clan leaders recognized that there was a law against FGM in Sweden and that they needed to co-operate to avoid any of their members coming into conflict with the law. This was a good strategy as FGM work is very stressful. Now the worker has the support of the community leaders behind her and can also come out of the community and be supported by the Refugee Council. Another important issue is that the Refugee Council is supporting the community with other settlement problems, such as housing and immigration issues. Thus, the community feels that its culture is not so much under attack as they see the Refugee Council as a friendly organization which gives something to the community. It is likely, however, that the Refugee Council will get into conflict with the community if it becomes directly involved in child protection measures. So child protection work should be separated from community education projects. Another agency should deal with such work.

The communities should be informed of child protection policy in their area and space should be made available for them to discuss all aspects of child protection. Social services should prepare basic information material on the role of the local authority in child protection in relation to all forms of abuse, including FGM. They should inform communities what their powers are and solicit co-operation from the community. Should this not occur, opportunists within the community will play on the fears of the people and spread rumours and myths about child protection interventions. In Cardiff in the UK, the social services department got round this problem by carefully preparing pamphlets explaining what they do and what they do not do to inform the community and to allay their fears. The commonest one is that 'social workers are out to take your children away from you'. Appropriate support must be given to parents to help them adjust to raising children in a different environment.

YOUNG ADOLESCENTS

Young adolescents who have undergone genital mutilation need extra support. Spaces should be available for them outside the community so that they can come together to support each other. They also need to be able to go in and to come out of the community as they wish. In most cases these girls need role models of women professionals, particularly black women professionals, to encourage and to push them to exploit their potential. Black women feminist groups can be a major source of support for these children. In the UK, FORWARD International has encouraged many young women to take up professional courses so that they will be economically independent. One girl qualified recently as a social worker.

In Western countries there are developed systems of child care and child protection which can be used to speed up the eradication of genital mutilation of girls in the Western world. If one can put aside the politics surrounding FGM, and get to the people at grassroots level, one will find that the issue is not as complex as it seems. It is a question of helping families to lay to rest a redundant and harmful practice. With concerted effort in the Western world the eradication of FGM should not take more than two generations. With the major conflicts and civil wars in Africa, many refugees and their children from areas in Africa where FGM is widely practised are now in the West. Some of the most practical development aid that the West could offer African women would be to protect the girls growing up in the West from genital mutilation. When the wars and conflicts are settled many refugees and their girls who have not undergone genital mutilation will go back to Africa and, no doubt, exert some influence on the campaigns to eradicate FGM there. They will come with a new perspective of womanhood free from the pain of genital mutilation. This is the plea of African girls.

7

CONCLUSION AND DIRECTIONS
FOR THE FUTURE

'Violence against women shall be understood to encompass, but not be limited to, the following... female genital mutilation and other traditional practices harmful to women... States should condemn violence against women and should not invoke any custom tradition or religious consideration to avoid their obligations with respect to its elimination. States should pursue by all appropriate means and without delay a policy of eliminating violence against women..'

(Declaration on Violence Against Women adopted by the UN
General Assembly in December 1993).

Historically all societies have devised different methods for the repression of female sexuality, among the most extreme and brutal of which is mutilation of the erogenous zones of the female sexual organ. The roots of the practice of FGM can be found in the patriarchal family and in society at large. Religion is used by chauvinists to reinforce the practice. Paradoxically, women who are victims of FGM are the gate keepers of the practice in their communities. This can only be understood within the context of their general powerlessness in male-dominated societies. Women receive social approval and rewards for undergoing FGM. Over the years they have come to view mutilation of their genitals with pride and the pain involved as a necessary step in growing up. Social and economic sanctions are meted out to those who do not comply with female genital mutilation.

Female genital mutilation has major short- and long-term physical and psychological health risks. In the past it has been a 'sensitive' issue and very difficult to tackle. It had remained in a cultural cul-de-sac and minimal action had been taken by governments and international organizations involved with women and children's well-being towards ending the practice. The United Nations was the first to raise FGM at an international level but nothing really happened until Western feminists took up the issue during the UN Women's Decade (1975-85). Although this provoked a backlash it brought the subject back into the international arena and, since that period, there has been slow but steady progress in breaking down the walls of silence surrounding the practice. The contributions of individuals, feminists and NGOs to this process have been remarkable and gradually the subject has emerged from its cultural ghetto to become an item on the health and human rights agenda.

The most pleasing development is that women and men from African countries are now leading the campaign for its abolition. With few resources, they have embarked on awareness-raising campaigns and have managed to break the taboo surrounding FGM in their communities and within countries. As a result, there is increased awareness of the practice in Africa and the subject is open for discussion. In parts of the Middle East and the Far East and Latin America, where FGM has been reported, work has hardly begun to study the extent of the practice and to initiate education campaigns for its abolition. In the main, millions of girls continue to undergo genital mutilation in rural areas and amongst the urban poor. The estimate of girls at risk of genital mutilation – 6,000 per day in Africa alone – is staggering.

FGM is no longer a localized practice. Civil war and ethnic conflict has forced people to migrate to countries where the practice of FGM has been abandoned or was unknown. This has presented new challenges for health care and social work professionals. In Western countries, preventive work on FGM is advanced in the UK and France, where women's organizations have been campaigning against the practice for more than a decade. Work is just beginning in other Western countries.

Genital mutilation of girls has become an international issue –

a public health hazard and an emergency children's human rights problem. The greatest determination, combined with sensitivity and understanding of local conditions, will be needed if it is to be abolished. In every country and region where mutilations are carried out, the situation is different, likewise the political will to deal with FGM varies greatly at both local and national level. In Western countries, with more resources and developed child protection laws, the way forward is relatively clear. In Africa, where female genital mutilation is practised on a massive scale, the problem is more profound and the economic and political conditions vastly difficult, while international agencies are just beginning to explore their potential role.

To date, nearly all programmes have been individual, non-governmental or *ad hoc* efforts, with little integration into existing structures, minimal evaluation or monitoring, and little in the way of long-term goals and strategies. To achieve real change will require more planning, and more sustained commitment from governments and international organizations.

IN AFRICAN COUNTRIES:

- The abolition of female genital mutilation is the responsibility of governments and requires political will. While voluntary organizations can play a valuable role, it is only governments which can act to initiate and co-ordinate action.
- Governments should adopt a clear national policy for the abolition of FGM.
- Governments should establish an inter-agency team incorporating members from relevant government departments, NGOs working in the field and professionals to follow up action on FGM.
- Mass education using all available channels of communicating information to the public should be targeted and tailored to the community and should use appropriate cultural mediums to formulate a strong and unambiguous message against the practice. This can be achieved through integration into adult literacy programmes, development programmes, through the activities of already existing community organizations,

women's groups, through specific workshops, radio, TV, churches and mosques,the trade unions, etc.

- Legislation to back up the information campaign will be needed but it can only function fully with the development of a parallel child protection system which identifies children at risk of mutilation and moves swiftly to protect them. This is a potential area for prevention; social services departments should explore this.
- In areas where female genital mutilation takes place within the setting of group initiation ceremonies, governments should establish procedures for timely anticipation of these ceremonies and for assisting the communities to celebrate puberty rites but without the genital mutilation of young girls.
- Ministries of Health should initiate epidemiological studies to identify the types of FGM practised in each country, and mortality and morbidity rates associated with female genital mutilation.
- Government hospitals, clinics and medical centres should not practise any form of female genital mutilation. There should be in-service training to upgrade the knowledge of doctors, nurses, paramedics, administrators, etc. with regard to the health consequences and the legal and social implications of the practice.
- Health professionals' bodies should lay down disciplinary measures for professionals who practice female genital mutilation.
- The prevention of female genital mutilation should be integrated into primary health care – in Maternal Child Health (MCH) clinics, health promotion, family planning and public health information. Sex education and counselling on sexual health problems should be an important part of health promotion.
- There should be supervision and control of traditional excisors. Alternate sources of income should be provided. Excisors can be integrated into the primary health care system by retraining them to be central in women's health promotion activities in their communities.
- Women's organizations with different perspectives of approaches but complementing each other's work on the eradication of FGM should be supported.

- As FGM is performed to please men, men should be brought into the campaign. They should be informed of the undesirability of FGM and sex education for men that breaks down the myths and fears surrounding female sexuality should be promoted.
- Religious leaders should be co-opted into the campaign but until there is one clear message from religious leaders, that FGM in all its varieties is totally unacceptable, the public will continue to be confused. This can be solved by convening a world conference on religion and FGM in Africa where all world faiths should be represented. Feminist religious leaders and scholars should also be present. All religious leaders with their varying viewpoints should be represented and a final decision by vote should be taken at this conference.
- There should be intensive education against the practice in schools, colleges, teacher training programmes, etc. Gender and sex education introduced at school will help in the long term to promote women's human rights, break down the myths surrounding female sexuality and promote healthy adult sexual relationships.
- Good practice should be strengthened, publicized, promoted and integrated into training programmes.
- There should be a programme of education on the human rights of women and children, using means such as literacy programmes, gender training, extension workers in schools, radio, TV, women's clubs, etc.
- Every year there should be a government-backed 'day of action' on women's health, including the issue of violence against women.

IN WESTERN COUNTRIES:

- Governments should recognize female genital mutilation is a complex form of child physical abuse practised on babies and young girls, and should not incorporate female genital mutilation as a harmless cultural practice within policies promoting multi-culturalism.
- Governments should adopt a clear policy on the abolition of

female genital mutilation and give directives to local government, local authorities, states, counties and districts to act.

- The Ministries of Health should undertake research into the
epidemiology of FGM in order to identify the numbers of
women and girls who have already undergone FGM, the types
and health problems associated with the practice. The numbers of girls at risk of FGM should be identified.

- Local government, etc. should develop an anti-racist policy on
female genital mutilation. A specific department, e.g. the
social services department, should be given a mandate to co-
ordinate activities within a given area on female genital mutilation.

- Community consultation should take place and the viewpoints and vulnerabilities of the community should be taken
on board in policy development on female genital mutilation.
However, the welfare of the girl child and her right to protection from genital mutilation should be paramount. The child
would need a special advocate on committees developing policies on the prevention of female genital mutilation.

- Local response to female genital mutilation should be multi-
pronged with education as the foundation of any strategy to
abolish female genital mutilation.

- There should be clear and unambiguous legislation against the
practice of female genital mutilation. Where it is incorporated
into existing laws against assault, this must be made clear to
the communities directly concerned and to professionals
involved with child health and child protection. Any ambigui-
ty will foster the idea in the community that FGM is an
acceptable practice and professionals will be unable to work
on the issue.

- The prevention of female genital mutilation should be incorporated into the framework of the protection of children from
abuse. However, the focus on child protection should be on
education and counselling. The law should be used as the last
resort.

- Guidelines and protocols for inter-agency co-operation and for
intervention will always be needed, as well as training which
provides professionals in health, social work, education, police

child protection officers and the legal profession with in-depth knowledge about the practice and the appropriate skills for prevention.

- Race awareness training will be needed for all professionals. This will facilitate a sensitive and an anti-racist approach to dealing with female genital mutilation and it will enhance professional skills.
- In the case of threatened female genital mutilation, professionals should act quickly and effectively to protect children. Children should immediately be placed on the 'at-risk' register and an experienced social worker should be attached to the family. The focus in child protection should be preventative, educational and persuasive. Children should be removed from families only as a last line of defence. Legal action through the police and the courts should be the last resort.
- Child protection interventions should be sensitive but firm. They should provide support by helping refugee families find solutions to other problems they face in adjusting to a new environment.
- Children who are found mutilated should not be taken away from their parents or be put on the child protection 'at-risk' register. However, this should alert professionals to focus on the protection of younger siblings in the family who might be at risk of FGM.
- As a priority, local government or local authorities should act as catalysts and open space within communities practising female genital mutilation for community education. Communities should be empowered and given resources to engage in community education for themselves. Community education should incorporate information on the legal status of the practice of female genital mutilation, child protection laws in the country and information for women with complications arising from FGM to access health care delivery.

A key area of community education will be the involvement of religious leaders in the anti-FGM campaign. The problem of religion and its position on FGM has been underlined.

- All newly arrived communities who practise female genital mutilation should be given information, counselling and support to readjust to a new environment. Within the resettlement policy they should be informed of legislation against the practice and of child protection mechanisms to protect the child from all forms of abuse.
- Parallel to community education, there should be health promotion and counselling against female genital mutilation by professionals. This should not be viewed as an intrusion into a minority culture but as part of improving health service delivery to minority groups.
- The key professionals in the frontline for health promotion are midwives during the ante-natal period, public health nurses, paediatricians who work with families with young children, school nurses, social workers and general practitioners. When fully trained these professionals can play a key role in monitoring children at risk of female genital mutilation and will be in a position to act to protect children. This should not be seen as racist intervention but as protecting the black female child from abuse.
- Resources should be made available to rehabilitate women who have already undergone genital mutilation, including protocols for de-infibulation, gynaecological/psycho-sexual help, together with individual and community counselling.
- Adolescent girls who are infibulated need special support and space to express themselves, to be reassured and to seek help for any gynaecological or psychological problems they may be facing. They must be supported in developing an identity which takes on board the best of the two worlds – the world of their parents and the world where they are growing up.
- Black and other groups independent of the communities and acting as pressure groups on health and catalysts specializing in child protection and FGM, providing a base for information and training and acting as a bridge between the professionals, the family and the community, are critical for change in Western countries. They should be fully funded by the Departments of Health and by local government.

INTERNATIONAL AGENCIES

More governments are openly condemning female genital mutilation and FGM is progressively becoming less sensitive as a policy issue. Still, financial and technical support from international agencies will be needed for the campaigns for the eradication of FGM.

- Programmes should be well-funded and properly planned. They should be preceded by pilot projects to determine feasibility and to avoid wastage of resources. They should have short and long-term goals and be subject to independent evaluation and monitoring. Programmes should concentrate on finding practical solutions at grassroots level and should integrate all aspects of the problem – health, education, welfare, tradition and custom, women and children's rights, development.

- Women's health care should be an integral part of any aid given by donor governments to the health programmes of international agencies. Emphasis should be placed on the currently neglected areas of gynaecological, mental and non-maternity health needs of women as persons in their own right.

- All development workers in countries where female genital mutilation is practised, including those working in refugee camps, should be trained to be aware of the issue and should be willing to discuss constructive solutions with local communities, women's organizations, health professionals, government officials and others.

- All development programmes, including those working with men, should incorporate education, awareness-building and moves to raise the status of women. A positive and supportive attitude from men can decisively influence the abolition of female genital mutilation.

The UN Specialized Agencies

WHO, UNICEF and UNFPA have started to have some input in the eradication of FGM. They can do more. WHO, UNICEF,

UNFPA, UNESCO and UNDP should each allocate 0. 5% of their total expenditure in the period 1994-2000 on programmes to combat female genital mutilation.

WHO
The WHO has expressed interest in collaborating with governments. Its strengths lie in the following areas:
1 Research related to prevalence, types and consequences of FGM and disseminating information about the findings.

   WHO has the potential to reach out to international development agencies, professionals, field workers, etc. with special information packages which will help advance the campaign. There were nearly 50,000 people at the UN Population Conference held in September 1994 in Cairo. These were people working in the field with women and families. A similar number will attend the Women's Conference in Beijing in 1995.
2 Support for the training of health workers at all levels, including obstetricians/gynaecologists, paediatricians, midwives and nurses to raise their awareness of the health consequences of FGM, how to deal with complications arising from FGM and assist professionals in the integration of prevention into primary health care.
3 Setting standards and providing guidelines on many confusing aspects of current work on FGM, e.g. classification of the different types, research methodology and coordination of research.
4 Initiating pilot research programmes on the eradication of FGM and convening evaluation workshops to strengthen current approaches to the eradication of FGM.
5 Strengthening NGO activities with training and back-up with information material.

UNICEF
Practices such as genital mutilation and forced early marriages of girls are basically to do with the rights of the girl child. These practices persist not solely out of ignorance but through gender discrimination. They also have an economic base. In relation to the latter, both practices are linked to the bride price. Some par-

ents look forward to receiving the bride price when their daughters are given away in marriage. No amount of health education on its own will be sufficient to persuade parents who are motivated by economic gain to abandon the practice. The education programmes will need to be backed with legal and child protection measures.

Child health monitoring systems will need to be strengthened and child care law and mechanisms for child protection developed so that the state can intervene in abusive practices affecting children. It is currently assumed that abusive practices such as sexual abuse of children, emotional neglect and gross physical abuse do not exist on a large scale in Africa because of the nature of the extended family structure. Gross physical abuse of children, severe beating for example, can be restrained by other adult members of the family, but since no studies have been done in this area, one cannot be sure what is happening. There is also rapid social change and African traditional societies are breaking down very fast.

In my opinion the area of harmful traditional practices, such as forced marriages of girls and female genital mutilation, will benefit from child protection systems, but this can only be brought about through government policy, including legislative measures.

The rights of children are central to UNICEF's mandate. UNICEF can collaborate with governments in the following areas:

1 Strengthening social services departments and children's societies to develop their infrastructure on child monitoring and to protect children from harmful traditional practices such as FGM at grassroots level. This should go hand in hand with the education measures.

2 Strengthening the training of staff from social services departments so they can protect girl children from all harmful traditional practices.

3 Supporting the funding of specific posts within social services departments to focus on harmful traditional practices affecting girls.

4 Supporting the funding in country programmes for the abolition of FGM.

AID DONORS

Genital mutilation of girls should be adopted as a major human rights and a health issue of the 1990s. Aid donors have a right and a duty to become involved in its prevention and to place pressure on the relevant governments to undertake effective measures to eradicate it.

In areas where more than 50% of the female population undergo genital mutilation, resulting in major physical and psycho-sexual problems for girls and women and placing extra burdens on already inadequately resourced health care and delivery, aid given towards health programmes should be tied to proven measures taken by governments to abolish female genital mutilation.

THE INTERNATIONAL PUBLIC

Genital mutilation of girls is primarily a violation of the fundamental human rights of girls and later on of adult women. The abuse of children can never be a private issue, as children do not have a voice. The international public who want to help should not be intimidated. Many nationalist struggles, e.g. the dismantling of apartheid in Africa or the release of political prisoners incarcerated in African jails would not have been possible without the contribution of the international public. There is already the stirring of an international movement against FGM. This movement needs to grow. People who do not come from FGM-practising communities but who want to be active in the campaign can join anti-FGM organizations which offer scope for international membership. These organizations will be able to help them to contribute effectively to support those nationals from countries directly concerned and in the forefront of the campaign for abolition. Examples of organizations and projects offering scope for such contributions are:
● The African Resource Centre, Ottawa, Canada,
● Equality Now, New York, USA,
● The Supporters Group, FORWARD International, London, UK,
● Swedish Sister-To-Sister Programme, Radda Barnen (Swedish Save the Children), Stockholm, Sweden.

.The international public, whose money supports aid pro-grammes, have a responsibility to request information on those programmes funded by donor governments and international agencies to eradicate female genital mutilation. This should include independent statistics showing the reduction of the inci-dence of the practice within countries. Any information on FGM being practised to your knowledge should be sent to the UN Centre for Human Rights and to the relevant anti-FGM pressure groups.

AFRICAN GRASSROOTS FEMINISTS AND HUMAN RIGHTS ACTIVISTS

Much has been said about focusing on economic development for women as the priority for improving women's status. Howev-er, without liberation of the mind this might be quite difficult to achieve. Women in all societies have internalized their oppres-sion. The status of women will not be altered very much in Africa and other developing countries unless women themselves change their consciousness and become willing to fight for their rights, which are enshrined in their countries' constitutions and within international law. In some countries, where fundamentalism is developing fast, this might be difficult, but in many areas there is room for grassroots activism around the following issues:

Reproductive rights include the right to control their fertility, the right to control their bodies and their sexuality, to evolve meaningful systems in their communities to deal with violence against women, to redefine themselves as women without genital mutilation, to choose who they want to marry, to review the bride price, to stop customary demands for proofs of virginity at marriage, to engage in a feminist interpretation of the religious texts and to develop all this with the full participation of grass-roots women, to gather data on the abuse of women at grassroots and to link in with regional and international women's human rights organizations, etc.

Consciousness-raising at grassroots level and activism by women reformers in the community backed with legal reforms will facilitate social change and improve the status of women. It is an area which is difficult to penetrate, but the development of work in the community is pivotal to improving the status of women in traditional patriarchal societies. International agencies should not shy away from supporting feminist activities by women from developing countries, particularly Africa.

There is a gap between introducing women's human rights issues into international human rights agendas or into national agendas and giving them meaning in the lives of women. Women and Law in Development in Africa is one of the few women's human rights networks helping grassroots women to gain access to their legal rights as enshrined in their countries' constitution. Women need income-generating programmes, family planning services, maternal child health care, but they also need consciousness-raising. Education should lead to liberation not domestication!

African women leaders should not accept a fragmented approach to women's health and development. There is much international goodwill towards the campaign for abolition of FGM. Women leaders should seize this opportunity to galvanize women at grassroots level and at the workplace into a true women's health movement. This is the time for it. Such a movement will provide space for women to discuss their health issues including all forms of violence against women within the family and in society in a holistic manner. This can also discuss reproductive rights and the right of women to control their bodies, sexuality and so forth.

Practices such as female genital mutilation persist for many reasons. One important reason is women's denial of their deeply buried pain and their wish to avoid confronting it. The inability to understand women's lives and to facilitate the processes which will help women to deal with this pain means that FGM continues into the next generation, and the next generation. Giving information, discussing, counselling, consciousness-raising, should be a major input of a women's health movement. This will help women find a new identity for themselves outside the context of genital mutilation. It will facilitate the breakdown of generational cycles of abuse. What is needed is group activities which help women lay to rest old rituals of passage which prepared them to fit into male-dominated societies and to discover new forms of initiation which prepare them for life in the 1990s and beyond.

The mobilization of women into a grassroots women's health movement would not be so difficult as women are mobilized already on many fronts, e.g. wings of national political parties, religious women's organizations, trade unions, literacy programmes, development programmes, clans and so on. It is only en masse that women will be able to confront overt patriarchy. The good news is that in almost all African countries' governments have set up women's ministries with a mandate to promote women's rights. Women should call upon this mandate to promote their interests.

Finally, African grassroots feminist activists working in the field need to be supported, to network, to exchange ideas and to come together to support each other. They should network with grassroots feminists in Latin America, India and in Western countries. There is much to be learnt from each other. Latin American women are good at mobilizing at grassroots level. Equally, Indian women are fighting traditional patriarchal oppression in a different context, but their experiences are similar in many ways to those of African women. Poor Western women are fighting for economic survival within rich patriarchal economies. The hardships faced by black women living in Western ghettos, particularly in the USA, are sometimes worse than those faced by women in developing countries. It is their experiences and struggles which link women together. Grassroots feminists should make links with international grassroots women's human rights organizations such as Equality Now (New York) who have been supporting women to find a voice within forums such as the United Nations, and to lobby for women to access international resources.

BUILDING UP A GRASSROOTS INTERNATIONAL WOMEN'S HUMAN RIGHTS ORGANIZATION

We have seen the contribution that powerful human rights organizations such as Amnesty International have made to addressing human rights abuse – torture, perpetuated by governments on citizens. Most of the abuses women face, including FGM, are committed in the home. They are condoned by the family and by patriarchal society. The human rights abuse of women is accepted as culture and tradition. It is citizen upon citizen abuse which is happening every day to millions of women and girls round the world. The mainstream human rights organizations have failed to respond to gender-based violence within the family. It is women globally who have put gender-based violence on the UN Human Rights agenda and on governmental agendas. Women are not going to wait for mainstream international human rights organizations to adjust to their needs. It will not happen in the next decade. FGM is only a tip of the iceberg.

It is important that women across cultures build their own powerful international human rights organizations which can respond to the needs of women at grassroots level. Such organizations will make links with grassroots women activists, gather independent data on the human rights abuse of women around the world, provide this information to the United Nations Commission on Human Rights and also the UN Commission on the Status of Women, to bring pressure to bear on governments, and other relevant institutions to see to it that women's human rights are respected. That is the only way forward.

APPENDIX

Contact organizations and advocacy groups

There are a growing number of groups and organizations engaged in anti-FGM campaigns around the world. Not all of them can be listed here, so this is a select list of organizations and advocacy groups which provide information. All organizations can be contacted directly for information, unless stated otherwise.

African Centre for Democracy and Human Rights
Karaiba Avenue
K.S.M.D.
The Gambia
ACDHR publishes a newsletter which covers human rights issues, specifically dealing with African women. FGM has been discussed in its newsletters. The Centre hosted a workshop in February 1994 on the theme of African women and tradition, culture and religion. For information, and ideas from the recommendations of the seminar, write directly to the Centre.

African Resource Centre
1719 Bank Suite 301
Ottawa
Ontario K1V 724
Canada

AIDOS (The Italian Association for Women in Development)
Vie del Giubbonari, 30
00186 Rome
Italy
AIDOS has produced a multimedia modular training package on FGM which is useful for trainers. It also has a Somali video on FGM which has proved useful with the Somali communities.

CAMS International (Commission Internationale pour l'Abolition des Mutilations Sexuelles)
BP 11,345
Dakar
Senegal
CAMS, a feminist organization, has a membership open to all women internationally.

CAMS French Section
6, Place Saint-Germain des Pres
75006 Paris
France
CAMS in France, has made some ground in the justice system by bringing criminal prosecutions. It provides advice on the law and FGM and has recently released an education video which can be used with immigrant groups.

Equality Now
226 West 58th Street
New York, NY 10019
USA
This grassroots organization, led by women lawyers, has a broad international membership. The group collects data on women's human rights abuses globally and also launches campaigns.

Focal Point for Human Rights of Women
United Nations Centre for Human Rights
Palais des Nations
CH-1211 Geneva 10
Switzerland
The UN Commissioner on Human Rights has appointed a Special Rapporteur on violence against women. Individuals and organizations are encouraged to submit information directly to the Centre.

FORWARD International (Foundation for Women's Health Research and Development)
Africa Centre
38 King Street
London WC2B 8JT
UK
FORWARD publishes training materials which are useful for professionals in a variety of areas, including health care, social work, education, community development and research. FORWARD also provides training on policy and intervention strategies and support. The African Well Woman Clinic for free obstetric and gynaecological care can be accessed through Forward.

IAC (Inter-African Committee on Traditional Practices Affecting the Health of Women and Children)
P.O. Box 3001
Addis Ababa
Ethiopia
LIAISON OFFICE:
147 Rue de Lausanne
CH-1202 Geneva
Switzerland
This African women's umbrella organization, made up of national chapters and affiliates in 24 countries, provides training materials and undertakes advocacy work and information campaigns.

IPPF (International Planned
Parenthood Federation)
P.O. Box 759
Inner Circle
Regent's Park
London NW1 4LQ
UK

Minority Rights Group
379 Brixton Road
London SW9 7DE
UK

NANNM (National Association
of Nigeria Nurses
and Midwives)
National Secretariat
P.O. Box 3857
Ikeja Post Office
Lagos
Nigeria

PAI (Population Action
International)
1120 19th St, NW
Suite 550
Washington, DC 20036
USA

Radda Barnen (Swedish Save
the Children)
S-107
88 Stockholm
Sweden

RAINBOW (Research Action
Information Network for Bodi-
ly Integrity of Women)
P.O. Box 1554
Cooper Station
New York
NY 10276
USA

The Royal College of Nursing
20 Cavendish Square
London W1M 0AB
UK
*The RCN has produced material
on FGM for nurses and midwives.*

The Women's Health Book
Project
The Hesperian Foundation
2796 Middlefield Road
Palo Alto, CA 94305
USA
*The Hesperian Foundation has
prepared a women's health book.*

WIN News (Women's International Network News)
187 Grant Street
Lexington, MA 02173
USA
*WIN News produces a regular col-
umn on FGM as well as distribut-
ing the* ChildBirth Picture Book
free to African groups on request.

World Health Organization
Division of Family Health
CH-1211 Geneva 27
Switzerland
*WHO has produced a useful
information pack on FGM.*

NOTES AND REFERENCES

Chapter 1
Introduction

1   Alan David, *Infibulation en République de Djibouti*, Thesis No: 131, Université de Bordeaux, L'Amicale des Étudiants en Médecine de Bordeaux, 1978.
2   Anne de Villeneuve, 'Étude Sur une Coutume Somalie', Les Femmes Cousues, *Journal de la societe des Africanistes* 1937,7.
3   Jacques Lantier, *La Cité Magique*, Editions Fayard, 1972 (translation by Scilla Mclean).
4   Gérard Zwang, 'Mutilations sexuelles féminines. Techniques et Resultants', *Female Circumcision, Excision and Infibulation*, ed. Scilla Mclean, Minority Rights Group Report No. 47, December 1980.
5   The London Declaration, The First Study Conference on Genital Mutilation of Girls in Europe, organized by FORWARD (Foundation For Women's Health Research and Development), London, 6-8 July 1992.
6   Tsehanesh Gudeta, 'The Silent Shame' *Private Decisions, Public Debate*, Panos Publications, London, 1994.
7   Asma El Dareer, *Woman why do you weep? Circumcision and its consequences*, Zed Press, London, 1982.
8   Ibid.
9   Assitan Diallo, *L'Excision en Milieu Bambara*, unpublished thesis for the École Normale Superieure, Bamako, Mali, p.20.
10 Asma El Dareer, op.cit p.8.
11 This information was conveyed to the author by Zelalem Oldjira in a lecture for graduate students studying for the Masters Programme on Maternal Child Health at the Institute of International Child Health, London University, 1994. Zelalem Oldjira is a primary health care nurse trainer with the Ethiopian Evangelical Church, Ethiopia, 1994.
12 Efua Dorkenoo and BAFROW background research for, *A proposed women's health promotion project with a focus on the prevention of genital mutilation – a working model for the West African region*, FORWARD, London, 1993.
13 Report of the UN Commission on Human Rights, Review of further Developments in the Field with which Sub-Commission has been concerned, *The study on Traditional Practices Affecting the Health of Women and Children*, Forty-third Session, July 1991, p. 19.
14 Rev. Canon Ephantus Josiah, *Female Circumcision*, Uzima Press, Nairobi, undated, p.15.
15 Ibid.

16 Dr Leila Mehra, WHO, intervention at the Symposium on Female Genital Multilation in the Netherlands, Leiden, organized by the Consultancy For Maternal Health and Family Planning, 2 October, 1992.
17 Helen Davidson and Andrew Alderson, *Mutilation doctor banned, Sunday Times*, 28 November, 1993.
18 Symposium on Female Genital Mutilation in the Netherlands, organized by the Consultancy For Maternal Health and Family Planning, Leiden, 2 October, 1992.
19 Ibid.
20 Alison Boulton, 'Calls for Female Circumcision on NHS Sparks Storm', *The Observer*, 14 February, 1993.
21 Mario Belo from Portugal put forward a motion to make it possible for immigrant women to practise female genital mutilation without interfering with their customs, European Parliament, Committee on Women's Rights, Palais de L'Europe, B.P. 1024, Strasbourg, 2 May, 1994.
22 Dr Tsehai Berhane Sellassie, *Man's World, Woman's Position, The Case of the Darasa widow.* N.EA, vol. 1. No.1.
23 Report on excision in Burkina Faso, National Committee on Traditional Practices, presented at the regional meeting of the Inter-African Committee on Traditional Practices affecting the health of women and children, Addis Ababa, April 1994.
24 Robert A. Myers *et al*, 'Circumcision ; its nature and practice among some ethnic groups in Southern Nigeria', *Soc. Sci. Med.*, vol. 21, no.5, 1985, pp. 581-8.
25 Ellen Ismail *et al*, *Women of the Sudan*, EIS Bendestorf, Germany, 1990.
26 FORWARD's casework files, 1992. A 25-year-old white woman was married to a Somali man in the north of England. The woman said she was encouraged by women in the husband's family to undergo infibulation and this was performed by a midwife from the community. She regretted the decision later on, the marriage broke down and she sought advice from FORWARD on how to get medical help.
27 John Muganda, 'Women circumcised by force', *Standard on Sunday*, Kenya 3 January 1993.
28 Toni Y. Joseph, 'One who defied tradition', *Essence Magazine*, July 1992, p. 62.
29 FORWARD casework files, 1989.
30 Jacques Lantier, *La Cité Magique,* Editions Fayard, 1972 (translated by Scilla Mclean).
31 Dr Ahmed Abu-el-Futuh Shandall, Faculty of Khartoum, 'Circumcision and infibulation of females', *Sudanese Medical Journal*, 1967, Vol. 5, No. 4, Dr. J.A. Verzin, 'The sequelae of female circumcision', *Tropical Doctor,* October 1975.
32 From documentary *Scarred for Life,* ABC News, Day One Show, 1993.
33 Amnesty International British Section Bulletin Jan/Feb 1994, p. 20.
34 Judy Mann, 'Torturing Girls Is Not A Cultural Right', *Washington Post,* 23 February, 1994.
35 Miriam Kahiga, 'One Rite, Too Many Wrongs', *Daily Nation,* 3 and 5 April 1994.
36 Dr Mohamed Warsame, 'Medical and Social Aspects of Female Circumcision in Somalia', in the Proceedings of the International Seminar on Female Circumcision, AIDOS, Somalia, 13-16 June 1988.

37 W.I. Onuigbo, 'Primary vaginal stone associated with circumcision', *Obstet. Gynecol.*, Vol.44, 1974, pp. 769-70.

38 W.I. Onuigbo, 'Vulval epidermoid cysts in the Igbos of Nigeria', *Arch. Dermatol.*, Vol.112, 1976, pp. 1405-6.

39 M.I. Asuen, 'Maternal Septicaemia and death after circumcision', *Tropical Doctor*, 1977.

40 Dr Ollivier reproduced by Renée Saurel, *L'Entrerrée Vive* VII in *Les Temps Modernes*, Febuary, 1980.

41 Dr Asma A. El-Dareer, *Female circumcision and its consequences for mother and child*, Yaounde, 12-15 December, 1979.

42 Rodney Hedley and Efua Dorkenoo, Child Protection and Female Genital Mutilation, *Forward*, 1992, p. 6.

43 Adrienne Burgess, 'The user's guide to the clitoris', *Cosmopolitan*, October 1993, p. 172.

44 Ibid.

45 Ibid.

46 Shere Hite, *The Hite Report*, Dell Books, New York, 1976.

47 Dr Nahid Toubia, *Female Genital Mutilation, A Call for Global Action*, 1993, Women Ink., NY, 1993.

48 Shandall, op. cit. p. 188.

49 Hanny Lightfoot Klein, *Prisoners of ritual. An odyssey into female genital mutilation in Africa*, The Haworth Press, New York, 1989.

50 Dr Sami A. Aldeeb Abu-Sahlieh, *To mutilate in the name of Jehovah or Allah. Legitimization of male and female circumcision*, unpublished research, Institute of Canon Law, University of Human Sciences, Strasbourg, France, 1994.

51 Dr Maher Mahran, *Les risques medicaux de l'excision (circoncision medicale)*, reprint of a paper published in *Bulletin Medicale de l'IPPF*, Vol. 15, No. 2, April 1981.

52 Dr Sami A Aldeeb Abu-Sahlieh, op. cit. p. 29.

53 Dr Mohammed Badawi, 'Epidemiology of female sexual castration in Cairo, Egypt', *Truth Seeker*, July/August 1989.

54 Ibid.

55 Ibid.

56 *Female genital mutilation*, information pack produced by the Division of Family Health, World Health Organization, Geneva, May 1994.

57 R Ghadially, 'All for Izaat: the practice of female circumcision among Bohra Muslims', *Manushi*, No. 66, New Delhi, India, 1991.

58 Enquiries from British white women to FORWARD on casework files, who have had female circumcision (cutting the hood to release the clitoris) performed for cosmetic reasons, 1991, London.

59 Abed Asali *et al*, *Ritual Female Genital Surgery Among Bedouin in Israel*, Beersheva Mental Centre, PO Box 4600, Israel.

60 Dr Asma A. El Dareer, University of Khartoum in a communication to a symposium on 'The changing status of Sudanese women', 23 February, 1979.

61 Hanny Lightfoot-Klein, op. cit.

62 FORWARD casework files, 1994.

63 Dr Taha Ba'asher, *Psychosocial aspects of female circumcision*, paper presented to the Symposium on the Changing Status of Sudanese Women, 23 February 1979.

64 Saffiatu Kassim Singhateh, *The incidence of female circumcision in the Gambia and its effect on women and children,* in Proceedings of the international seminar on female circumcision, Mogadishu, 13-14 June 1988, AIDOS, Italy.

65 These feelings of rejection are articulated by Kenyan girls in 'The silence over female circumcision in Kenya', in *Viva,* August 1978.

66 Val Simpson, 'There is something missing, I am not a real girl,' in *Mirror Woman,* 20 February 1991.

67 FORWARD casework files, 1991.

68 Dr Nahid Toubia, *Testimony on Female Genital Mutilation,* given to the Subcommittee on International Organizations, and Human Rights, Congress of the United States, Committee on Foreign Affairs, House of Representatives, US, September 1993.

69 FORWARD casework files, 1994.

Chapter 2
The practice

1 Raqiya Haji Abdalla Dualeh, *Sisters in Affliction,* Zed Press, London, 1982 (now out of print).

2 The Bible, Gospel according to St Matthew, chapter 19, verse 12, Authorized King James version.

3 Robin Morgan and Gloria Steinem, *International Crime of Genital Mutilation,* first published in *Ms Magazine,* March 1979.

4 Ibid.

5 Ibid.

6 Ibid.

7 Ibid.

8 Ibid.

9 Ibid.

10 Louise Carpenter, 'Intimate plastic surgery' , *Company* magazine, April, 1994, p. 68.

11 Joanna Pitman,'City Lights', *The Times* Magazine, February 1994.

12 Fran P Hosken, *The Hosken report on genital and sexual mutilation of females, Fourth revised edition,* WIN NEWS, 1993.

13 Dr Nahid Toubia, *Female genital mutilation. A call for global action,* Women Ink, NY, 1993. See also Table 1.

14 Ibid.

15 World Health Organization, Resolutions and Decisions, Executive Board, Ninety-third session, Geneva, 17-26 January 1994, page 208.

16 University of Khartoum 1979, World Fertility Survey 1979/80.

17 Dr Asma El Dareer, *An epidemiological study of female circumcision in the Sudan,* M.Sc. thesis, Department of Community Medicine, University of Khartoum, Sudan 1980/81.

18 Fran P. Hosken, op. cit. See appendix for full breakdown of ethnic groups practising FGM in Africa.

19 Dr Sami A. Aldeeb Abu-Sahlieh, *To Mutilate in the Name of Jehovah or Allah – Legitimization of Male and Female Circumcision,* unpublished research document, the Institute of Canon Law, University of Human Sciences, Strasbourg, France.

20 Communicated to the author by midwives attending a midwifery refresher course in London, 1994.

21 Dalia Ben-Air, *Naomi – A Prize-winning Portrait Wizo Review*, Fall/Winter, 1993.
22 Abed Asali, Naif Khamaysi, Yunis Aburabia *et al*, *Ritual Female Genital Surgery Among Bedouin in Israel*, Beersheva Mental Health Centre, PO Box 4600, Beersheva, Israel, 1992.
23 Jerome Pasteur, *Selva Sauvage*, Editions Filipacchi, 1989.
24 FGM Appeal, Letter on File of EQUALITY NOW, NY, 1993.
25 Belkis Woldes Giorgis, *Female Circumcision in Africa*, ST/ECA/ATRCW.
26 The First National Conference on Genital Mutilation of Girls in Europe, organized by FORWARD, London, 6-8 July, 1992.
27 Marie Assaad, *Female Circumcision in Egypt-Current Research and Social Implications*, American University of Cairo, 1979.
28 AIDOS, documentary of FGM, *Seven Drops of Blood*, Rome, Italy.
29 James DeMeo, *The Geography of Genital Mutilations, The Truth Seeker*, July/Aug 1982.
30 Ibid.
31 Professor Ahmad Watik Pratiknya, *Female Circumcision in Indonesia: A Synthesis profile of cultural, religious and health values*, proceedings of the International Seminar on Female Circumcision, Mogadishu, Somalia, 13-16 June 1988.
32 James DeMeo, op. cit.
33 Ibid.
34 Information obtained from Dr Sander J. Briener, M.D.,F.A.P.A., Associate Professor Psychiatry, Michigan State University and Assistant Professor Psychiatry Wayne State University, US.
35 Sylvie Epelboin and Alain Epelboin, 'Ancient Beliefs and Obscure Origins', *People*, Vol 6, No. 1 IPPF, 1979.
36 Ibid.
37 Ibid.
38 Assitan Diallo, *L'Excision en Milieu Bambara:* unpublished thesis for the École Normale Superieure, Bamako, Mali.
39 Robin Morgan, op. cit.
40 Aminata, D. Traore, Ministere de la Condition Feminine, Abidjan, Ivory Coast, *Eléments pour une autre method d'approche de l'excision'* presented to the African Symposium on the World of Work and the Protection of the child, Yaounde, 12-15 December 1979.
41 Esther Ogunmodede in a background paper prepared for the first edition of MRG Report *Female Circumcision, Excision and Infibulation; the facts and proposals for change*, 'Female Circumcision in Nigeria'.
42 Dr Asma A. El Dareer, *Female Circumcision and Its Consequences for Mother and Child*, paper presented to the African Symposium on the World of Work and the Protection of the Child, Yaounde, 12-15 December 1979.
43 Dr Ahmed Abu-el-Futuh Shandall, *Circumcision and Infibulation of Females*, Sudanese Medical Journal, 1967, Vol. 5, No. 4.
44 Dr Sami Aldeeb Abu Sahlieh, op. cit.
45 Sheikh Dr Abdel Rahman al Naggar, 'Islam and Female Genital Mutilation', Workshop on Traditional Practices, End of UN Decade for Women, NGO Forum, 1985.
46 Dr Sami Aldeeb, Abu Sahlieh, op. cit.
47 Ibid.

48 Fran P. Hosken, 'FGM — Strategies for Eradication,' *The Truth Seeker*, July/August 1989.
49 Rev. Canon Ephantus Josiah, *Female Circumcision*, Uzima Press, Nairobi, undated.
50 Ibid.
51 Jomo Kenyatta, *Facing Mount Kenya*, Vintage Books, New York, 1965.
52 Assilan Diallo, *L'Excision en milieu Bambara*, unpublished thesis for the École Normale Supérieure, Bamako, Mali, p. 20.
53 Isatou Touray unpublished MA Thesis, *Reconceptualizing Traditional Practices in the Gambia, The Case of Female Genital Mutilation, Women and Development Programme*, The Hague, October, 1993.
54 Ibid.

Chapter 3
What are the issues?

1 The late Thomas Sankara, Chairman of the National Revolutionary Council, Head of State, Burkina Faso, extracts from the statement on female genital mutilation recorded at Ougadougou, 1983 in UN Economic and Social Council Report, Commission on Human Rights, Forty-second session, 3 February 1986.
2 R.W.J. Austin, *Islam and the Feminine in Islam in the Modern World*, ed. Dennis MacEoin and Ahmed Al-Shahi, 1983, quoted in B.A. dissertation *Female Genital Mutilation, A Tradition of the Repression of Female Sexuality in Egypt*, Elizabeth Healy, Social Studies, The University of Newcastle Upon Tyne.
3 Esther Ogunmodede in a background paper, *Female Circumcision in Nigeria*, prepared for the first edition of the Minority Rights Group Report No. 47, *Female Circumcision, Excision and Infibulation*.
4 Virginia Mak, 'Female Genital Mutilation – A Tradition of Pain,' *Health Sharing*, Winter/Spring, 1993.
5 Ibid.
6 'African Women and Human Rights,' *Africa Women*, a bi-annual development journal produced by Akina Mama wa Afrika, London, December, 1993.
7 Report of the UN Economic and Social Council, Commission on Human Rights, First Session, 18-22 March, 1985.
8 Ibid.
9 *Airing Africa's controversial subject*, West Africa publication, 5 October 1981.
10 Hanny Lightfoot-Klein, *Prisoners of Ritual, An Odyssey into Female Genital Mutilation in Africa*, The Haworth Press, New York, 1989.
11 Kate Millet, *Sexual Politics*, Virago, London, 1971.
12 The late Captain Sankara, op. cit.
13 Belkis Woldis Georgis, op. cit.
14 Ibid.

Chapter 4
International initiatives and action

1 Awa Thiam, *La Parole aux Negresses*, Editions Denoel/Gonthier, Paris, 1978. Quote translated into English by Scilla McLean in *Female Circum-*

cision, Excision and Infibulation: the facts and proposals for change, MRG Report No.47, 1980.
2 Scilla McLean, *Female Circumcision, Excision and Infibulation: the facts and proposals for change*, MRG Report No. 47, 1980.
3 Ibid.
4 Report of the United Nations Seminar on *Traditional Practices Affecting the Health of Women and Children*, ECOSOC, Commission on Human Rights, 12 June, 1991.
5 *Human Rights, the New Consensus*, Regency Press, London, 1994.
6 Ibid.
7 WHO seminar on *Traditional Practices Affecting the Health of Women and Children*, organized by WHO Regional Office for Eastern Mediterranean, in Khartoum, February, 1979.
8 In a formal statement to the United Nations Human Rights Commission, WHO assured governments of its readiness together with UNICEF to support national efforts against female circumcision, August 1982.
9 WHO expresses unequivocal opposition to medicalization of female genital mutilation in any setting to the United Nations Human Rights Commission, August, 1982.
10 Dr Asma El Dareer,' An Epidemiological Study of Female Circumcision in the Sudan', Department of Community Medicine, Faculty of Medicine, University of Khartoum, Sudan, 1980-1.
11 A.M. Rosenthal, 'A Major Advance in Cairo Against Genital Mutilation', *International Herald Tribune*, 7 September, 1994.
12 Scilla McLean, op. cit.
13 Information provided by Berhane Ras-Work, President, Inter-African Committee on Traditional Practices, August 1992.
14 Information on IAC given by Berhane Ras-Work, President of the IAC, at the 47th WHO Health Assembly, May, 1994.
15 Asma El Dareer, *Women Why Do You Weep?* Zed Press, London, 1982.
16 Awa Thiam, op. cit.
17 Raqiya Haji Dualeh Abdalla, *Sisters In Affliction*, Zed Press, London, 1982 (now out of print) and Asma El Dareer, *Women Why Do You Weep?* Zed Press, London, 1982.
18 Olayinka Koso-Thomas, *The Circumcision of Women: A Strategy For Eradication*, Zed Books, London, 1987.
19 Alice Walker, *Possessing The Secret Of Joy*, Jonathan Cape, 1992.
20 Alice Walker and Pratibha Parmar, *Warrior Marks*, Jonathan Cape, 1993.

Notes and references

Chapter 5
Africa – case studies

1 Marie Assaad, *Female Circumcision in Egypt: Social Implications, Current Research and Prospects for Change, Studies in Family Planning, Population Council*, Vol. 2, No. 1, pp. 3-16. Note similar remarks in Marie Assaad, *Villagers' Participation in Formal and Informal Health Services in the Village of Babel Wa Kafr, Hama, Tala County, Menoufia Governorate.*
2 Dr Sittana Hassan Ishagh *et al, Present Situation of Female Circumcision in the Sudan*, in the Report on a Seminar on Traditional Practices Affecting the Health of Women and Children in Africa, organized by the NGO Working Group on Traditional Practices Affecting the Health of Women and Children, Dakar, Senegal, 1994.
3 Ibid.
4 Ibid.
5 Sudan Demographic and Health Survey 1989/1990, Department of Statistics, Ministry of Economic and National Planning, Khartoum, Sudan.
6 Ibid.
7 Ibid.
8 Kwabena Gyan, *Background Paper on African Men Against FGM*, FORWARD files, July 1994.
9 Ibid.
10 Jennie Street, 'The nurse who did it', *The Bangladesh Observer*, Dhaka, 20 December 1989.
11 *Childhood Messages: Rights For Girls*, in CONTACT, a bi-monthly publication of the Christian Medical Commission and the World Council of Churches, No.131, June 1993.
12 Dr Olayinka Koso-Thomas, *The Circumcision of Women: A Strategy for Eradication*, Zed Press, London, 1982.
13 *Dangers of Female Circumcision*, Institute of Health Education, Dar-es-Salaam, Tanzania 1989.

Chapter 6
The Western world

1 Barbara Myles, *Health Matters*, BBC World Service, *March, 1991.*
2 *Abena Adomako, Refugee Women's Voices*, newsletter of the Refugee Women's Network, London No.6, June 1994, p. 6.
3 Val Simpson, 'There is something missing, I am not a real girl', *Daily Mirror*, Feb 20, 1991 and from the author's casework files 1989-1994.
4 Following the screening of the documentary *Cruel Ritual, Forty Minutes*, BBC2 21 February, 1991, two young women who spoke on the documentary were threatened by community members.
5 Ibid.
6 Joan Bakewell, BBC *Heart of the Matter, A Dangerous Silence*, January 1993. The author knows the details of this case as she was consulted on the case.
7 Personal information conveyed by an African mental nurse counsellor based in the US, who is using her own time to meet and to discourage African people from genital mutilation of girls, September, 1994.

8 Rodney Hedley and Efua Dorkenoo, *Child Protection and Female Genital Mutilation Advice for Health, Education, and Social Work Professionals,* FORWARD, 1992.
9 Lisa Beyer, 'Thou Shalt Not Mutilate', *Time,* October, 1989.
10 Ibid.
11 Helen Pitt, 'A knife in any language', *The Guardian,* 3 March 1993.
12 Louise Panton, *Female Circumcision, Forty Minutes,* BBC2, 3 March 1983.
13 Linda Green, *Concern Over Brutal Ritual,* METRONEWS July 16 1992.
14 Author was interviewed on Australian radio in December 1993. Articles on the case appeared in the following Australian newspapers: *Herald Sun* and *The Age,* 2 December, 1993.
15 Report from participants from Canada, in the First Study Conference on Genital Mutilation of Girls in the Europe/Western World, July 1992, London.
16 J. Haskey, *The Ethnic Minority Populations of Great Britain,* estimates by ethnic group and country by birth. Population trends, Office of Population Censuses and Surveys, London, *HMSO,* 1990:35.
17 Anne Nesbitt *et al, African Children in Britain,* 'Archives of Disease in Childhood, 1992; 67: 1402-1405.'
18 Congresswoman Pat Schroeder, 'Female genital mutilation – a form of child abuse', *The New England Journal of Medicine,* September, 1994, 311, 11.
19 Kendra Sone, 'Sexuality, Abuse and Culture', *Community Care,* June, 1992.
20 Rodney Hedley and Efua Dorkenno, op. cit.
21 FORWARD casework files, 1992.
22 Ibid.
23 FORWARD casework files, 1994.
24 The policy guide has been phrased from policy on FGM by the London Borough of Tower Hamlets, Lambeth and from the author's field experience.
25 *Female Genital Mutilation, the Unspoken Issue,* RCN, March, 1994.
26 Hindley and Montagu, *Female Genital Mutilation,* unpublished paper, Birmingham, 1994.
27 J. Tritten, 'Tricks of the trade', *Midwifery Today,* Autumn 1992, Eugene, Oregon, USA.
28 Hindley and Montagu, op. cit.
29 McCaffrey, M, *et al.* 'Management of Female Genital Mutilation – the Northwick Park Hospital Experience', Department of Obstetrics and Gynaecology, Northwick Park Hospital, Harrow, Middlesex.
30 Ibid.
31 Ibid.

SELECT BIBLIOGRAPHY

ABDALLA, Raqiya H.D., *Sisters in Affliction: Circumcision and Infibulation of Women in Africa*, Zed Press, London, 1982.

ADAMSON, Fiona, *Female Genital Mutilation: A Counselling Guide for Professionals*, FORWARD, London, 1992.

Aman, *The Story of a Somali Girl as told to Virginia Lee Barnes and Janice Doddy*, Bloomsbury, London, 1994.

DORKENOO, Efua, *Tradition! Tradition: A symbolic story on female genital mutilation*, FORWARD, London, 1992.

DORKENOO, Efua and ELWORTHY, Scilla, *Female Genital Mutilation: Proposals for Change*, Minority Rights Group, London, 1980, 1992.

EL DAREER, Asma, *Woman, Why Do You Weep? Circumcision and its Consequences*, Zed Press, London, 1992.

EL SAADAWI, Nawal, *Hidden Face of Eve: Women in the Arab World*, Zed Press, London, 1980.

HEDLEY, Rodney and DORKENOO, Efua, *Child Protection and Female Genital Mutilation*, FORWARD, London, 1992.

Human Rights the New Consensus, Regency Press in association with the United Nations High Commissioner for Refugees.

ISMAIL, Ellen and MAKKI, Maureen, *Women of the Sudan*, Verlag Dr Ellen Ismail-Schmidt, Postfach 1152, D-2106, Bendestorf, Germany.

KOSO-THOMAS, Olayinka, *The Circumcision of Women: A Strategy for Eradication*, Zed Books, London, 1987.

LEWIS, I.M., *Islam in Tropical Africa*, International African Institute in association with Hutchinson University Library for Africa, 1980.

LIGHTFOOT-KLEIN, Hanny, *Prisoners of Ritual: An Odyssey into Female Genital Mutilation in Africa*, The Haworth Press, New York, 1989.

ORTIZ-THOMPSON, Elizabeth, *Your Complete Guide to Sexual Health*, Planned Parenthood of San Diego and Riverside Counties, Prentice Hall, 1989.

Private Decisions, Public Debate: Women, Reproduction and Population, Panos Publications, London, 1994.

Report on a Seminar on Traditional Practices Affecting the Health of Women and Children, Inter-Africa Committee, Geneva, (undated).

Report on the Regional Seminar on Traditional Practices Affecting the Health of Women and Children in Africa, Inter-Africa Committee, Geneva, 1987.

Report on the Conference on Traditional Practices Affecting the Health of Women and Children in Africa, Inter-Africa Committee, Geneva, 1990.

RUTABANZIBWU-NGAIZA, Jean, *et al*, *Women and Health in Africa*, BPC Publication 6, London School of Hygiene and Tropical Medicine, London, 1985.

The State of the World's Children, UNICEF, 1994.

THIAM, Awa, *Black Sisters Speak Out: Feminism and Oppression in Black Africa*, Pluto Press, London, 1980.

TOUBIA, Nahid, *Female Genital Mutilation: A Call for Global Action*, Women Ink, New York, 1993

WALKER, Alice, *Possessing The Secret of Joy*, Harcourt Brace Jovanovich, New York, 1992.

WALKER, Alice and PRATIBHA, Parmar, *Warrior Marks*, Jonathan Cape, London, 1993.

INDEX

Abdalla, Raqiya, 81
Abu-Sahlieh, Aldeed, 37, 38
abuse, child, 125, 137-40, 145-6
adolescents, 158-9, 168; *see also* puberty rites
aesthetics, 31, 40
Africa: case studies, 83-121; family, 45-50; FGM abolition policy recommendations, 163-5; FGM prevalence, 31-2, 88-9; *map*, viii; women, position, 43-50; *see also names of countries*
African Centre for Democracy and Human Rights, 177
African Men Against Female Genital Mutilation, 78
age of FGM performance, 10, 12-13, 131
agencies, international, 3-4, 66-70, 169-72
aid donors, 169, 172, 173
AIDOS, 79, 119-20, 177
Akan, Ghana, 44
Amnesty International, 14, 70, 176
Assaad, Marie, 33, 83
Assad, Maurice, 96, 97
Australia, xi, 12, 76, 128, 188

Ba'asher, T.A. 24-5
babies: clitoris removed 8, 127-8
Babiker Bedri Scientific Association, 79, 86, 121
Badawi, Mohammed, 21-2
Bahrain, 32
Bambara, the, 34-5, 40
Banoub, Hedy, 96-7, 98
barbers, 8
Bedouin women, 23, 32
belief systems, 34-6, 46, 139, 148
Belo, Mario, 181

Belsey, Mark, 13
Benin, W, Africa, 98; FGM prevalence, 88-9
Bible, 30
Bohra, India, 22
Bojang, Rose, 102
boys 52, 54
breast-feeding, 35
Bristol 143-4
Brown, Isaac Baker, 30
Burkina Faso, W. Africa, 34, 181; FGM prevalence, 88-9; migrants from, 103; opposition to FGM, 98-100; Presidential statement, 43, 54; UN meetings, 63, 64, 79

Cairo Family Planning Association, 116
Cameroon, W. Africa, 100; FGM prevalence, 88-9
campaigning groups, 12-13, 151-2, 162, 168; *see also names of groups*
CAMS, 79, 80-1, 108, 177, 178
Canada, 76, 128
Cardiff, 158
Care of Girls Committee, 96, 97
cauterization, 8
Central African Republic, FGM prevalence, 88-9
ceremonies, 25, 39-40, 51, 164; *see also* puberty rites
Chad, W. Africa, 100-1; FGM prevalence, 88-9
chastity, 35, 47
chastity belts, 29
child abuse, 125, 137-40, 145-6
Child Abuse and Neglect, Congress on, 79

child protection, 87, 133, 137, 139-47, 158, 159, 164, 166, 167-8, 171; policy, 147-51

childbirth, after FGM, 2-3, 15, 16-17, 143; recommended procedures, 152, 153-4

children: education, 155-6, 165; rights, 56-8, 66, 72, 125, 170-1, 172; at school, 144, 145, 155-6; upbringing, 54, 96-7; *see also* babies; child abuse; child protection; girls

Childrens' Act, UK, 146, 149

China, 55

Christianity, 38-9; Roman Catholic Church, 38-9, 98, 99

circumcision: female 5, 22, *see also* female genital mutilation; male, 52, 54-5

clitoridectomy, 1, 3, 30-1, 52; for babies, 8, 128; prevalence, 32

clitoris: beliefs about, 34-5, 46; *described*, 17, 20-3; hood removal, 5, 22-3; removal, *see* clitoridectomy; *illus.*, 18, 19;

colonialism, 60, 63, 84

community education, 157-8, 163-4, 166,167, 168

contraception, 17, 35

Coomaraswamy, Radhika, 66

Copenhagen conference, UN, *1980*, 61-3

Coptic Orthodox Church, 39, 96, 116

Coulston, Michael, 78

counselling, 94, 124-5, 133, 143, 144-5, 154, 168

Cruel Ritual (TV documentary), 75, 187

culture, and migration, 131-3

cysts, 16

David, Alan, 2

de Villeneuve, Annie, 2

death: FGM after, 12; resulting from FGM, 14-15, 128, 149

Decade for Women, UN, 61-3, 74, 79, 162

de-infibulation, 24; clinical, 154-5; by husband, 13, 23; for menstruation, 16

DeMeo, James, 33

development, 58, 169

Diallo, Assitan, 40

Diop, Aminata, 12

Djibouti, 2, 9, 16, 32, 33, 115; FGM prevalence, 88-9

doctors: in Africa, 9, 53; in western countries, 10, 136, 142, 144-5

Dogon, the, 34-5

Doko, Upper Guinea, 104

drugs, 21

Drum (magazine), 80

dysmenorrhoea, 15, 16, 153

economics: excisors, 50-1; marriage, 47-9, 58, 171

education, 87, 143, 151, 165, 171; children, 155-6, 165; community, 97, 157-8, 163-4; women, 90, 92, 111

Egypt, 8, 12, 21, 33, 34, 40, 115-17; Cairo, seminars in, 70, 115-16; Coptic Church, 39, 96, 116; FGM prevalence, 88-9; women, 96-8

El Dareer, Asma, 75, 81

Equality Now 76, 175, 178

Eritrea, 27, 118, 125; FGM prevalence, 88-9

erogenous sensitivity, 20-4

Ethiopia, 8, 10, 117; Darasa group, 12; Falashas, 10, 32; FGM prevalence, 88-9; missionaries, 38

European Parliament, 10, 181

excision, 5, 15; *see also* female genital mutilation

excisors: in Africa, 8, 9, 50-1, 164; in western countries, 131

Falashas, 10, 32

family, African, 45-50, 54, 146-7; honour, 47, 145; *see also* mothers

Fatwa Committee, 38

fatwas, 37-8

female genital mutilation (FGM): *19C.* western, 30-1; definition, 4, 147-8; distribution, *maps,* viii-xi; instruments and operators, 8-9; motives and functions, 34-41, 51; origins, 32-3; physical consequences, 13-24; prevalence, 31-2, 88-9; psychological consequences, 24-7;

reasons for survival, 91, 92; types, 5-8; *see also* circumcision; excision; infibulation; *sunna*
feminists, 126-7, 158-9, 162, 175
fertility, 46; infertility, 16
fistulas, 15, 17
foot binding, 55
foreskin, 35, 52
Forty Minutes: Cruel Ritual (TV documentary), 75, 187
Foundation for Women's Health Research and Development (FORWARD), 76-8, 102, 178, 181; *1992* conference, 4, 76, 128-30
France, 79, 80-1, 127-8, 131, 162
Freud, Sigmund, 30, 34

Gachukia, Eddah, 111
Gambia, W. Africa, 8-9, 25, 77, 101-2; FGM prevalence, 88-9
gender oppression, 133-4; *see also* patriarchy
genitals: female, 6-7, 17-23, (*see also* clitoris; female genital mutilation; vulva); male, 52
Ghana, W. Africa, 3, 77, 102-3; FGM prevalence, 88-9; matrilineal societies, 44
Ghanaian Association on Women's Welfare, 102-3
girls: age of FGM performance, 10, 12-13, 131; upbringing, 54, 96-7
governments: in Africa, 84-7, 163, 165-6, 169; in western countries, 10; *see also* laws and legislation
grandmothers, 9, 49-50, 115
Guinea, W. Africa, 103-4; FGM prevalence, 88-9
Guinea-Bissau, W. Africa, 104; FGM prevalence, 88-9
Gulbet, Assefash, 93-4

Happy Family (magazine), 80
hashish, 21
health, 57-8, 60; holistic activities, 92; sexual, 17-24
health care services and workers, 60; in Africa, 9, 15, 16, 27, 93-4, 164; policy on FGM, 69; train-ing, 149-51, 170; in western countries, 142, 144, 152-3, 168; *see also* doctors; hospitals; midwives
Health Visitors, 142, 143
Hedrington, Connie, 104
Hesperian Foundation, 179
Hite, Shere, report by, 20
HIV, 14
honour, family, 47, 145
Hosken, Fran, 38, 79-80, 89
hospitals: in Africa, 9, 14-15, 16, 78;childbirth in, after FGM, 2-3, 153-4; Northwick Park, London, 78, 154
human rights, 10, 55-8, 59, 66, 67, 82,165, 176;
UN Commission on, 63-6, 72, 75, 79, 178; UN conference on, 56; *see also* children's rights; women's rights
hygiene, 14, 40
hymen repair, 31

immigrants, 181, 128, 137, 152, 168; second-generation, 124-5, 127, 136; *see also* minority communities; refugees
India, *map* x, 22, 55, 175
Indonesia, x, 32, 33
infertility, 16, 46
infibulation: ceremony, 25; childbirth, effects on, 2-3, 15, 16-17, 143, 152, 153-4; complications, 16-17; process *described*, 1-2, 5, 123; reinfibulation 17, 36; *illus.*, 7; *see also* de-infibulation; female genital mutilation
infibulation, intermediate, 5, 8
initiation rites, 39-40, 44, 51, 52
instruments used, 8; unsterile 14
Inter-African Committee on Traditional Practices, 69, 70, 73-4, 77, 79, 98, 100, 129, 178
intermediate infibulation, 5, 8
International Conference on Population and Development, 70
International Council of Nurses, 78
International Institute for Labour Studies, 81
International Planned Parenthood Federation, 179

international public, 172-3
Islam, 33, 36-8
Islington and Camden Health
 Authority, 156
Ismail, Edna Adan, 63, 118
Israel, 23, 32
Italian Association for Women and
 Development (AIDOS), 79,
 119-20, 177
Ivory Coast, W. Africa, 104-5; FGM
 prevalence, 88-9

Japan, 31

Kennet, Lord, 76
Kenya, E. Africa, 12, 15, 39, 71-2,
 111-13, 145-6; FGM preva-
 lence, 88-9; legislation, 9, 32;
 missionaries, 38-9
Kenyatta, Jomo, 39
Khartoum: Nursing College, 121;
 WHO seminar, 68, 75, 119,
 186
Koso-Thomas, Olayinka, 81, 110

Lantier, Jacques, 2, 13
Latin America, 32, 175; *map* ix
laws and legislation, 9-10, 64-5, 119,
 135-6, 145-7, 148-9, 164, 166
Lee, Janice, 155-6
Liberia, FGM prevalence, 88-9
Lightfoot-Klein, Hanny, 21
Linnander, Margareta, 71, 72
local authorities, 126, 136, 146, 158,
 166, 167; *see also* social services
London: Northwick Park hospital,
 78, 154; refugees in, 24, 144-6;
 social services, 125, 140-1, 144,
 145-7
London Declaration, *1992*, 4, 76,
 129

Mahran, Maher, 21
Malawi, 14
Malaysia, *map* x, 32, 131, 144
Mali, 8, 12, 34-5, 39, 40, 105-6, 128;
 FGM prevalence, 88-9
marriage: consummation, 23; defloration, 48, 96; de-infibulation
 on, 13, 23, 24; different ethnic
 groups, 12; economics of, 47-9,
 58, 171; forced, 48, 97; in

matrilineal societies, 44; polygamous, 35, 36
masturbation, 20, 22, 30
matrilineal societies, 44-5
Mauritania: FGM prevalence, 88-9
Mburu, Rosemary, 15
McCaffrey, Mary, 154
Meigs, Charles, 30
men: attitudes to FGM, 52-3, 54-5,
 83, 94,95, 97-8, 99, 165; circumcision, 52, 54-5; fathers,
 54, 125, 144, 145; project
 against FGM, 78; *see also* patriarchy
menopause, 17, 49-50
menstruation, 96; celebration, 44;
 impeded, 15, 16, 153
Middle East, 32
midwives: in Africa, as excisors, 51; in
 Sudan, 85; in Western countries,
 2-3, 143, 152, 153-4
migration: control, 136; and culture,
 131-3; *see also* immigration;
 refugees
minority communities, 133-4, 137-9,
 142, 145-7, 149-50, 166, 168
Minority Rights Group, 72, 74-5,
 112, 129, 179
missionaries, 38-9, 60, 98, 102
mixed race, 124
Moi, Arap, 39
Morgan, Robin, 30, 81
mothers: breast-feeding, 35; and
 FGM for daughters, 1, 8, 25,
 43, 46, 50, 123, 132-3, 140-1,
 144-5, 146-7; grandmothers, 9,
 49-50, 115; *see also* childbirth;
 matrilineal societies
Ms (magazine), 81
Muslims, x, 8, 32, 36-8, 93-4, 99,
 101,104, 109
Mustafe, M.A.S.: *quoted*, 1-2
MYWO, 112-13, 179
NANNM, 107, 179
Netherlands, 10
neuroma, 15
ngansingbas, 9
NGO Working Group, 71-3
Niger, W. Africa, 106; FGM prevalence, 88-9
Nigeria, W. Africa, 8, 12, 15, 32, 47-
 8, 106-8; FGM prevalence, 88-
 9; refugees from, 125

non-governmental organizations, 65, 70-82
Northwick Park hospital, London, 78, 154

Ogunmodede, Esther, 80, 106-7
Oldjira, Zelalem, 180
Ollivier, Dr, 16
Oman, 32
operators, 8-9
orgasm, 20-3, 34

Pakistan, *map* x
parents: consent, in UK, 16, 139, 144-5; *see also* family; mothers; patriarchy
patriarchy, 29-31, 40, 41, 45-7, 54, 175
police, 149, 167
politics, 12, 159
polygamy, 35, 36
Pratiknya, Ahmad, 33
pregnancy: apparent, after FGM, 16; FGM in, 15; treatment in, 143, 152, 153-4
pressure groups, 151, 168
prosecution, 149
prostitutes, 30, 36
psychiatric treatment, 24
psychological consequences of FGM, 24-7
puberty rites, 34, 39-40, 44, 51, 52, 94-5, 164

qat, 21
Qatar, 32

racism, 133, 134-5, 149-50, 152, 155, 167
Radda Barnen, 71, 112, 117, 129, 179
Ras-Work, Berhane, 72, 73
Refugee Council, 157-8
refugees 59; camps 31; in schools 155-6; in western countries, 12, 24, 128, 137, 140-1, 144-5, 157, 159 regulation of FGM, 9-10
rehabilitation, 168
re-infibulation, 17, 36, 155
religion, 36-9, 41, 95-6, 99, 101, 139,165, 167
research studies, 60-1, 69, 127, 164, 166, 170

rights: children's, 56-8, 66, 72, 125, 170-1, 172; parents' consent, in UK, 16, 139, 144-5; women's, 55-6, 57-8, 67, 173, 174-6; *see also* human rights
rites of passage, 34, 39-40, 44, 51, 52, 94-5, 164 rituals, celebration, 51, 132
Roman Catholic Church, 38-9, 98, 99
Rora Habab, 92-3
Rosenthal, A. M., 82
Royal College of Nursing, 77, 153, 179

sanctions, 45-6
Sankara, Thomas, 43, 54-5
Saudi Arabia, 32
Scarred for Life (TV film), 77, 132
schools, 144, 145, 150, 155-6, 165
second-generation immigrants, 124-5, 127, 136, 159
secret societies, 51, 109-10
Senegal, W. Africa, 8, 32, 108-9; FGM prevalence, 88-9;
seminar in, 72, 79
sexual intercourse after FGM, 13, 14, 15, 21-4, 26, 125; *see also* de-infibulation
sexuality, 2, 13, 14, 15, 34-6; enjoyment, 20-4, 95;
repression, 29-31
Shaltout, Mahmoud, 37
Shandall, Ahmed, 21, 36
Sierra Leone, W. Africa, 3, 109-10; FGM prevalence, 88-9
Skoptozy sect, 29-30
slaves, 29, 33
social services, in western countries, 125-6, 127, 137, 140-1, 142, 144-5, 146-7; FGM policy, 147-51, 158, 166, 171
socialization, 54-5
Somali Women's Democratic Organization, 79, 118-20
Somalia, 13, 15, 26, 32, 33, 40, 123-4, 132, 181; FGM prevalence, 88-9; marriage, 36, 48; operators, 8, 51; opposition to FGM, 63, 79, 118-20; refugees from, 24, 120, 128, 144-7, 157
South America, 32, 175; *map,* ix
Steinem, Gloria, 30, 81

street theatre, 97-8
Sudan 9, 12, 21, 23, 26-7, 31, 32, 33, 36, 69, 84-7; age of FGM, 10; FGM prevalence, 88-9; operators, 8; opposition to FGM, 60, 62-3, 71-2, 84-7, 120-1
Sudan Family Planning Association, 80, 85
Sudan National Committee on Traditional Practices, 120-1
sunna, 8, 21, 37-8
Sweden, 77, 119, 136, 157-8

Tagouna, the, 35, 39
Tanzania, E. Africa, 3, 113; FGM prevalence, 88-9
Terre des Hommes, 80
Tevoedjre, Isabelle, 71, 72, 98
theatre, street, 97-8
Thiam, Awa, 59, 80-1, 108
Tiendregeogon, Alice, 99
Togo, W. Africa, 110-11; FGM prevalence, 88-9
torture, 70
Toubia, Nahid, 26-7
Traditional Birth Attendants, 8, 73-4, 101, 117

Uganda, E. Africa, 114; FGM prevalence, 88-9
UNESCO, 66, 71
UNFPA, 70
UNICEF, 66, 69-70, 86, 88, 170-2
United Arab Emirates, 32
United Kingdom, 2, 76, 136, 158-9; FGM in, 10, 127, 128, 131, 181; Parliament, 76; *see also* London; social services
United Nations, 55-6, 57, 60-1, 161; Commission on Human Rights, 63-6, 72, 75, 79, 178; Convention on the Rights of the Child, 65, 72; Decade for Women 61-3, 74, 79, 162; Family Planning Association, 121; Specialized Agencies, 66-70, 169-72
United States of America, 30, 76-7, 175; African immigrants, 27, 125, 132-3; Agency for International Development, 76, 100; *map*, xi; Orificial Surgery Society, 30

urination, 14, 16

vaginismus, 24
Vienna Declaration, 56, 65-6
violence against women, 79, 161, 176; *see also* female genital mutilation
virginity, 35, 36, 47-8, 141; pseudo-, 31
Viva (magazine), 80
vulva, 4; after FGM, 16-17; scar formation on, 16; *illus.*, 6, 7

Walker, Alice, 81, 102
Warsame, Mohamed, 15
Warrior Marks (film), 81, 102
Weil-Curiel, Linda, 81
Western countries, 123-59; incidence of FGM, 126-8; policy on FGM, 147-51, 165-8; prevention of FGM, 131-47; recommendations 165-8; refugees in 12, 24, 128, 137, 140-1, 144-5, 157, 159 ; treatment of FGM, 152-5; *see also names of countries*
widows: burnt, 55; FGM for, 12
Wilkhu, Inderjit, 140-1, 150
WIN News, 179
women: African, position in society, 43-5, 47-9, 52, 58, 61, 173-4; consciousness-raising, 92-5, 173-5; Decade for 61-3, 74, 79, 162; education, 90, 92, 111; excisors, 50-1, 52; older, 49-50; rights, 55-6, 57-8, 67, 173, 174-6; violence against, 79, 161, 176; workshop for, 79; *see also* marriage; mothers; widows
Women and Law in Development in Africa,174
Women's Action Group Against Excision and Infibulation, 75, 76
World Health Organization, 10, 13, 22, 24, 60-1, 66, 69-70, 75, 170, 179; *1979* seminar, 68, 75, 119, 186

Yemen, 21, 32, 128
Yoruba, the, 32, 35

Zwang, Gérard 4